THE
SOVEREIGN

THE WORLD'S MOST FAMOUS COIN
A History and Price Guide

THE
SOVEREIGN

THE WORLD'S MOST FAMOUS COIN
A History and Price Guide

DANIEL FEARON

Price Guide compiled by
BRIAN REEDS

HILLDEN PUBLICATIONS

BONHAMS

Acknowledgements

The Publishers would particularly like to thank
Graham Dyer of the Royal Mint.
Without his help and exhaustive knowledge,
this book would not have been possible.

Many thanks to Michael Marsh
for the invaluable use of his numbering, lettering and
rarity systems used throughout the book.

A Hillden publication
Published in 2001 by Hillden Publications
Produced by Good Publishing
17 Windmill Drive, Croxley Green, Hertfordshire.

A catalogue record of this title is available from the British Library

ISBN 1 874371 14 8

Frontipiece illustration previous page:
Ian Rank-Broadley's preparatory sketch of the new Royal Effigy.

Designed by John Dunne
Printed and bound by Proost Ltd Belgium

CONTENTS

INTRODUCTION

Coin collectors have long enjoyed the study of monetary history, and the lure of gold takes us back to King Midas and beyond. In England the birth of our coinage, in both Celtic and Roman times, included gold. With the Saxon, Norman and Plantagenet kings there followed several centuries of a silver-based coinage, but the new wealth of the first Tudor monarch, Henry VII, saw the introduction of a coin of great merit. This 'mighty' gold coin was first issued in 1489 and it was named for the King - the Sovereign.

In 1816, following the uncertain financial years of the Napoleonic Wars, the British Government reintroduced the sovereign, and the new coin, with the value of one pound (or twenty shillings), was first struck the following year. The sovereign was to replace the guinea, a coin introduced early in the reign of Charles II, and whilst the main run of dates ended in 1799, there was a final 'one off' coin of George III struck in 1813, issued to pay the army in the wars against France and called the 'Military' guinea. As with the guinea before it, the sovereign was - and still is - struck in 22 carat gold. It has a diameter of 22 millimetres and a weight of 7.98805 grams, or 123.274 grains. It was to be the coin that would set the standard for world trade for a century, only giving way to paper money at the end of the Great War, and finally becoming a part of our numismatic heritage when the country came off the gold standard in the 1930s.

Today the gold sovereign is still struck by the Royal Mint, though only as a collector's item. The Mint is no longer in its prime and historical site alongside the Tower of London, having moved to Llantrisant in South Wales in the late 1960s, but the golden sovereigns it strikes are still very much the same coin of 1817. The monarch's head appears on the obverse whilst the St George slaying the dragon on the reverse is the original design of the famous Italian medallist, and engraver at the Royal Mint, Benedetto Pistrucci. For many reasons, both political and economic, the sovereign was not issued for each and every year from 1817 to the present date, but for the first century there is a complete run of dates.

With the discovery of gold in Australia, and after an experimental 'Adelaide' coinage, and a period of local 'Sydney Sovereigns', sovereigns of the British design were struck in new branches of the Royal Mint, first in Sydney, then Melbourne and Perth. Between 1908 and 1919 sovereigns were struck at the branch of the Royal Mint in Ottawa, in Canada. The Great War even saw one year's production in India, at the Bombay Mint. The final Imperial mint to strike gold sovereigns was that at Pretoria in South Africa, where the coins were issued for a number of years in the 1920s.

The coins struck at the Imperial mints are all easy to spot, as they are clearly designated with a mintmark: the Australian coins with the initials M, S, or P, of the mint cities, and the Canadian, Indian, and South African coins, with a C, I or SA, for their respective countries. The Royal Mint in London being, as it were, the parent, needed no identifying features added to its coins.

Some 500 million sovereigns were struck at the Royal Mint, and a comparable number at the branch mints. Of the billion sovereigns that ever existed in the past, the bulk have been melted down and either recoined or converted into bullion bars. It has been estimated that, at most, no more than one per cent of the total mintage is now in existence.

Of the approximately ten million sovereigns believed to exist, many will by now be in worn condition. Many others, exported to India and the Middle East, were pierced for bridal dowries; elsewhere countless sovereigns have been mounted or converted into jewellery. Thus the number of sovereigns in collectable grades is probably fewer than five million.

Some sovereigns, such as the 1819 coin, only turn up

every few years in the saleroom and consequently fetch very high prices regardless of their condition. Other dates and mintmarks are scarce or even rare, but every so often they turn up when banks and institutions release their stocks onto the open market. The collector armed with the knowledge of what to look for can - and often does - profit from that knowledge many times over.

Despite the fluctuations in the bullion price of gold, which have a capricious effect on purely bullion coins such as Britannias, Maple Leaves and Krugerrands, sovereigns tend to maintain their value because of in-built numismatic factors. These provide a cushion effect in all but the very commonest sovereigns, which trade at a fairly small percentage over their bullion value.

To put together a representative collection of sovereigns from 1817 to the present day would take several years and a not inconsiderable outlay of money. To form a complete collection of more than 350 different dates and major varieties can become the absorbing pursuit of a lifetime.

DANIEL FEARON

EDWARD VI

ELIZABETH I

HENRY VII

HENRY VIII

JAMES I

THE FIRST SOVEREIGNS

Gold has had immense appeal for all humanity since the dawn of time itself. However, gold of a known weight and purity, impressed with a symbol to guarantee its value, has only been in existence for 2,500 years. Croesus, King of Lydia, produced the first coins in the Western world in electrum or 'white gold' – a light-yellow alloy containing a high proportion of silver. In classical times iron spits and copper dumps might serve for domestic currency, but silver coins were used in larger transactions and gold was the favoured medium of trade between merchants of many countries. When the Roman Empire spanned the known world its gold coins were essential to imperial commerce, until the fifth century when the Empire was engulfed by barbarians and its coinage fell into disuse.

Europe of the Dark and Middle Ages relied on silver, employing units derived from the Roman denarius - hence the deniers of France, dinars of the Arab world, denars of Central Europe and, of course, the notation 'd' used for the old penny in English currency. Twelve silver pennies were tariffed at one solidus, and twenty solidi were reckoned to be worth one pound (libra in Latin). This system survived in Britain in the £sd currency until 1971, but in medieval times the libra and solidus were only money of account, and for all practical purposes the penny was the only coin.

As trade progressed and economic and political stability emerged, the nation states of Europe found a need for larger denominations. From this resulted larger silver coins, culminating in the gulden groschen of the fifteenth century and the crowns, thalers and dollars of the sixteenth and later centuries.

Early Gold Coins

Gold re-emerged as a currency medium in the thirteenth century. The sack of Byzantium in 1204 gave Venice possession not only of an immense gold reserve, but also a virtual monopoly of the lucrative overland trade to India and Cathay (China). The Italian city states profited by this trade, for which gold coins were required, and this led to the development of the florins of Florence and the sequins (zecchini) of Venice, setting the pattern followed by other countries.

In England there were isolated examples of gold pennies from the eighth century onwards. It is thought that these exceedingly rare coins were minted as a tribute to the Pope, or for presentation to foreign heads of state. These coins, in effect, were regarded as a status symbol; they were struck for purposes of prestige and did not serve any economic necessity, as international trade did not require them at that time. The first serious attempt to issue a gold coin for trading purposes came in 1257, when Henry III issued a gold penny weighing 45 grains and tariffed at 20 silver pence. It failed, perhaps because the wrong tariff was chosen, but there was insufficient gold in the King's Treasury to provide for a substantial issue, far less a large enough volume of international trade to maintain a steady supply of gold for recoining.

By the late thirteenth century, however, a permanent gold coinage was becoming established in several European states, and by the 1340s it had become imperative for England to follow suit in order to keep in the commercial race. In January 1344 Edward III authorized the florin, containing 108 grains of gold and tariffed at 6 shillings. It was a failure because it was over-valued in relation to silver and had a real value of only 5s 1d. Within a few months it was replaced by the noble, containing 138.46 grains and tariffed at 6s 8d. This seems an odd amount, but in fact it represented half a mark, or a third of a pound, and thus united the two systems of money of account then in commercial use. It succeeded because it realistically reduced the ratio of silver to gold, from 12.59:1 to 11.04:1. In 1465 the noble was replaced by the angel of 6s 8d and the ryal of 10 shillings, each being accompanied by halves and quarters.

The noble, angel and ryal were struck in 'fine' gold and enjoyed a wide measure of acceptance which was remarkable, given the fact that England had been embroiled in the Hundred Years War with France and latterly was torn by the internecine strife of the Wars of the Roses. This prolonged series of civil wars came to an end in 1485 with the defeat of Richard III at Bosworth and the emergence of Henry Tudor as Henry VII. It is to this monarch that we are indebted for the first gold coin to bear the name of sovereign, introduced over 500 years ago.

The Development of the First Sovereign

Several factors played an important part in the evolution of this large and very handsome coin. First of all, there was the commercial penetration of West Africa by the Portuguese and other seafaring nations in the second half of the fifteenth century, which was intensified by the discovery of the rich hoards of gold along the Guinea Coast (now Ghana). In the 1480s, therefore, there was a dramatic influx of gold from this area into northern Europe, particularly the Low Countries, with England lagging not far behind. In 1487 the Emperor Maximilian, acting as Regent for his son Philip the Handsome, ordered the Dordrecht Mint in Holland to strike large gold pieces, known as the real d'or or grote reaal. The Emperor was depicted full-face, seated on a throne, crowned and holding the orb and sceptre of sovereignty.

Henry Tudor, then Earl of Richmond, spent much of his time in exile in the Netherlands and imbibed the manners, culture and commercial influence of the Low Countries before seizing the English throne in 1485. He was not slow in imitating Maximilian. By 1489 Henry had consolidated his position, and the input of Guinea gold provided the means for a grand political gesture. By an indenture of that year he ordained that the pound, hitherto merely money of account, was to be represented by a new gold coin, the largest struck in England up to that time.

This coin, tariffed at 20 shillings (when the shilling itself was only money of account - the first shilling coins being half a decade in the future) or 240 pence, weighed 240 grains of almost pure gold. Only two of these gigantic coins were to be struck in every pound of gold converted into coin, the remainder being struck as angels and half-angels. Although barely a handful of these sovereigns, as they were termed, has survived to this day, it has been estimated that as many as 50,000 may have been struck between 1489 and 1509, still a relatively small proportion of the gold output of that period. It is probable that the sovereign was regarded as a propaganda medium, used to project a certain image of Henry VII to the world at large. Extremely rare examples exist of the sovereign struck on flans of double or treble weight, and these are regarded as having been intended for presentation to courtiers and foreign dignitaries, who would doubtless have been greatly impressed. In May 1502, an example of such a gift was recorded in the book of payments of John Heron, treasurer of the Chamber: 'Ambassador of Hungary over and besides 10 sovereigns, £53 13s 4d'. Another Ambassador of Hungary 'over and besides 6 sovereigns £34 0s 0d'.

The political overtones are unmistakable in the design of both obverse and reverse. The former featured a full-length facing portrait of the King enthroned. Although obviously modelled on Maximilian's great coin, the sovereign surpassed it in sheer magnificence and exuberant detail. The elaborate decoration of the throne and the King's raiment - even the

Henry III, gold penny

Edward III, noble

ornament on the sceptre - were incredibly detailed. The King's head was deliberately enlarged, but the vacant expression and wildly-flowing locks maintained the stereotyped convention of royal portraiture which had endured since the time of Edward III two centuries earlier.

As the obverse, so also did the reverse surpass the brilliance of the real d'or. Whereas the latter had a crown surmounting a plain spade shield showing the Imperial spread-eagle, Henry's sovereign of 1489 placed a crowned shield over a highly elaborate Tudor rose. The overall effect of this was most pleasing and, while filling every part of the field, helped to focus attention on the heraldic shield in the centre. These coins were undated, but bore a mintmark that gives us their chronological sequence. Only one example has been found of the original issue of 1489, bearing a cinquefoil device. The second rarest type bears the cross fitchee adopted in 1492.

Five types of sovereign, differing in the details of both obverse and reverse, were struck during the reign of Henry VII and production peaked in the last year of his reign (1508-9), when £122,683 worth of sovereigns were minted. Sovereigns were also struck in the reigns of Henry VIII and his son Edward VI. Latterly, 'fine' sovereigns were issued during the reigns of Mary and Elizabeth I tariffed at 30 shillings. Henry VII sovereigns were all tariffed at 20 shillings although they were struck in 20, 22 and 23 carat gold.

Thereafter the name 'sovereign' disappeared. In the long reign of Queen Elizabeth I (1558-1603) the gold coin of 20 shillings was known simply as the pound, perhaps because 30 shillings was a sovereign. James I briefly revived the term sovereign for the gold 20 shilling pieces of 1603-4 as there was no longer a 30 shilling coin. When the rose ryal was introduced at a value of 30 shillings the unite, whose name

and design were aimed at the unification of the King's dominions of England and Scotland, became the name for the 20 shilling gold piece. Later gold 20 shilling coins were known as laurels (1619), unites (1625) or broads (1656). The gold pounds of Charles II rapidly acquired the name of guineas, alluding to the source of the gold imported by the African Company.

The Shortage of Silver

The guinea continued to be worth 20 shillings as late as 1688 and the overthrow of James II, but by that time the bimetallic system, whereby gold and silver were equally legal tender for any amount, began to collapse and gold to rise in value. Though still nominally worth only 20 shillings before the Glorious Revolution that ousted King James, the guinea rose to 21s 6d at the beginning of the reign of William and Mary. It eventually peaked at 30 shillings in 1694-5, before being pegged at 21 shillings in 1717, at which level it remained more or less constant for the rest of its career.

For almost two centuries, Spain in particular and western Europe in general had benefited from the fabulous riches imported from the New World, and the economies of the principal trading nations had come to be heavily dependent on this supply of precious metals continuing. Almost as soon as the first shipments of gold and silver had reached Spain at the beginning of the sixteenth century, prices rose sharply in Andalusia and inflation had a knock-on effect throughout the Iberian peninsula. Spanish industry priced itself out of the European market and, as a result, Spain had to rely more and more heavily on its bullion imports, which drained out of the country almost as quickly as they had arrived, thanks to aggressive and grandiose foreign policies pursued by successive rulers. The Low Countries, and latterly France, the German principalities and England, benefited in turn from Spanish largesse, but inevitably became infected with the same Midas syndrome. Everywhere, as the supply of gold and silver increased, prices and wages rose - though not usually synchronized, so that great hardship came in the wake of affluence.

When the bullion supply from Latin America began to dry up in the second half of the seventeenth century, Spain, which had gambled on precious metal futures, came perilously

THE SOVEREIGN SINCE 1817

At first, greater attention was given to the more pressing problem of the subsidiary silver coinage, and it was not until 1817 that production of gold sovereigns commenced.

There were important changes in the senior personnel of the Mint at the same time. Lewis Pingo and the French Nathaniel Marchant, both now in their seventies, were pensioned off in 1815, to be replaced by two members of the remarkable Wyon family. Peter George Wyon, a German who had worked as engraver at the Cologne Mint, came to England in the reign of King George II. His son George had four sons, all of whom worked as medallists and engravers. The eldest was Thomas Wyon (1767-1830), who – although not a Mint employee - was appointed as Chief Engraver of H.M. Seals. His brothers, Peter, George and James, worked in Birmingham and Dublin as medallists. The eldest son of Thomas Wyon, who bore the same name, was appointed Chief Engraver at the Royal Mint with effect from 16th August 1815. Almost a year later, on 25th May 1816, his cousin William Wyon (1795-1851), son of Peter, was appointed Second Engraver at the Mint.

In accordance with its very long tradition of employing foreign artists and craftsmen, the Royal Mint appointed Benedetto Pistrucci, an Italian cameo and gem engraver. On 16th June 1816 Wellesley Pole wrote to the Lords of the Treasury as follows:

'I have thought it desirable to employ Mr Pistrucci, an artist of the greatest celebrity and whose works place him above all competition as a gem engraver, to make models for the dyes of the new coinage and I request your Lordships' authority to pay Mr Pistrucci such remuneration as may be deemed necessary for his works. It is my intention that the models of Mr Pistrucci should be engraved in Jasper from which our Engravers will work in Steel and the models will be deposited in the Royal Mint and remain there with the Dies and Proof Impressions of the several coins.'

The Treasury sanctioned Pistrucci's employment on 26th June 1816. Eight years later, Wellesley Pole (now Lord Maryborough) reported that Pistrucci had been introduced to him by Sir Joseph Banks, adding: 'he submitted to me a Head of his late Majesty engraved in Jasper, which I approved and purchased as a Model for the New Coin'. In the six-month period to the end of 1816 Pistrucci supplied the Mint with three jasper cameos of the King's head, and a wax model of St George and the Dragon which was used for the reverse of the crown. For this work Pistrucci was paid the sum of £312 8s.

To Pistrucci himself goes the credit for having suggested St George and the Dragon as a suitable motif for the gold coins. Wellesley Pole approved the idea and commissioned Pistrucci to prepare a model, for which he was paid one hundred guineas. Some dissatisfaction had been expressed at the steel dies engraved by Thomas Wyon from Pistrucci's models, for the new silver coinage, so it was agreed that Pistrucci himself should engrave the dies for both obverse and reverse of the gold coins.

He had previously modelled in wax a cameo of St George slaying the Dragon, which was used in the production of the George in the insignia of the Garter made for the Earl Spencer. Now he extensively modified this for the coinage. At that time Pistrucci lived at Brunet's Hotel in Leicester Square, and he used a young Italian waiter there as the model for St George.

During 1817 Pistrucci reworked the steel dies for the silver coinage. In fairness to Thomas Wyon, he was a very sick man by that time and died on 22nd September. Pistrucci also engraved the dies for the gold coins, and his emoluments for that year amounted to no less than £1,322 5s 6d. On Wyon's death, the office of Chief Engraver fell vacant. The problem of employing a foreigner was neatly solved, as a later Master of the Mint subsequently reported:

'Finding no person of equal abilities with Mr Pistrucci, whose talents had now been directed to engraving upon Steel, it was understood to be his Lordship's [Lord Maryborough] wish that the office should be bestowed upon him but upon a reference to the Act of Limitation (12th and 13th Will. III) it was found to be incompetent for Mr Pistrucci, as a Foreigner, to hold an office of Trust under Government. This was explained to Mr Pistrucci by Lord Maryborough but at the same time his Lordship intimated to him that he should be glad to retain his services in any way that was compatible with the Laws of the country. In the Indenture of the Mint, a provision is made which authorizes the Master "as often as need shall require to take up as many Engravers to grave the Irons as shall be needful". Although Mr Pistrucci could not be placed upon the Establishment of the Mint, he might under the authority of the Indenture, be employed provisionally by the Master of the service of the coinage then carrying on. Accordingly the office of Chief Engraver was kept vacant and Mr Pistrucci was retained under an agreement which was understood to be as follows, Viz.: Mr Pistrucci, tho' not actually appointed, was in effect to execute the office and fulfil all the duties of Chief Engraver. He was to furnish all the Models and engrave all the Dies that might be ordered by the Master of the Mint for the Coinage. He was to receive for his services £500 per annum, being the salary allowed to the Chief Engraver, and he was to be permitted to occupy the House in the Mint allotted to that officer.'

Two men prominent in the reform of the currency were William Wellesley Pole (right), Master of the Mint and elder brother of the Duke of Wellington and the second Earl of Liverpool (left), Prime Minister and himself Master of the Mint from 1799 to 1801.

King George III
1760-1820

The design of the new sovereign was approved by an Order in Council of 18th June 1817, following a submission made to the Prince Regent on 31st May:

'I beg leave to lay before Your Royal Highness a Design for the Sovereign or Twenty Shilling Piece, having for the Obverse Impression the Head of His Majesty with the Inscription Georgius III D.G. Britanniar Rex F.D. and the date of the year, and for the Reverse the Image of St George armed, sitting on horse back encountering the Dragon with a Spear, the said device being placed within the ennobled Garter bearing the motto "Honi soit qui mal y pense". The Piece to be marked on the edge with the new invented graining.'

Actual Size

Page 14:
Sketch of the obverse design for the new George III sovereigns, 1817.

The obverse of the sovereign featured a right-facing profile of George III, his hair short in the contemporary fashion, but wearing the laurel crown of a Roman emperor. The legend GEORGIUS III D:G: BRITANNIAR: REX F:D: (Dei Gratia Britanniarum Rex Fidei Defensor - By the Grace of God King of the Britains, Defender of the Faith) ran round the outside. 'Britains' in the plural referred to Great Britain and Ireland, politically welded into the United Kingdom since 1800. 'Defender of the Faith' was the title conferred on Henry VIII by Pope Clement in 1521 for his defence of the seven sacraments against Martin Luther. Although this title had appeared on the Great Seal of England since the time of Henry VIII, it was not added to the coins of the realm until 1714. The date appeared below the truncation of the neck. A distinctive feature of the George III sovereign was the size of the lettering, which was taller than usual and had the effect of crowding the head so that the truncation almost touches the letters.

The reverse showed the figure of St George, naked but for his plumed helmet from which flowed a streamer, and depicted with the broken shaft of a spear in his right hand. The rest of the weapon lay on the ground below. He was reining in his spirited steed, which was trampling on the Dragon lying belly up in its death throes. This motif, in the best neo-classical tradition of the period, was enclosed in the Garter inscribed with the motto which may be translated as 'Evil be to him who evil thinks'. Under the broken spear are the tiny letters B.P., initials of Benedetto Pistrucci, and the initials W.W.P. (William Wellesley Pole) appear on the buckle.

The edge was grained and the coin had a thickness of 0.067 inch and a diameter of 0.868 inch. The coin contained 916.66 per thousand parts of pure gold, alloyed with 83.33

A pen and ink cartoon by James Prinsep, 1817.

parts of silver and copper to produce 22 carat fineness. The weight, fineness and dimensions of the sovereign have remained unchanged to this day.

Sovereigns were struck in the original design each year from 1817 to 1820. Sovereigns of 1817 and 1818, with mintages in excess of 3.2 and 2.3 millions respectively, are rated as normal, although examples in the better grades are elusive. Only 3,574 sovereigns were minted in 1819. Normal conditions were restored in 1820, but mintage figures are difficult to determine for this year due to continuous striking into 1821. The 1819 sovereign is arguably the rarest of the entire series. The auction records reveal only three specimens: a fair condition, which was sold by Spink & Son on 6th December 1984 for £3,100; a worn, pierced specimen that was sold at Glendining's in 1999 for £4,100; and a specimen in good condition sold at Sotheby's in October 1998 for £50,000. In total six specimens are known, and one possible proof.

George III sovereign, 1819.

King George IV
1820–1830

Although George IV reigned for only ten years, there were two quite different types of sovereign in that period. This reflected the ongoing struggle within the Mint, between Pistrucci, Wyon and the Masters of the Mint. A French engraver, Jean Baptiste Louis Merlen, was recruited on 11th February 1820 as assistant to Pistrucci, at a weekly salary of £3 3s for the first month and £4 4s thereafter. At that time the only other engraver on the Mint staff was William Wyon. Merlen was apparently hired at Pistrucci's specific request. Wellesley Pole again evaded the Statute of Limitation by appointing Merlen as an Extra-Assistant Engraver - hence the weekly salary instead of the customary annual emolument. His position later became more stable, and his salary was paid quarterly; but he remained in 'temporary' employment at the Mint for almost a quarter of a century. When he retired in 1844, at the age of 75, he was granted a pension of £136 10s a year. Those had been stormy years, when Merlen was occasionally caught up in the constant feuding between Wyon and the irascible little Italian.

Merlen was eventually responsible for the reverse dies of most of the coins of George IV, but both obverse and reverse of the sovereigns dated between 1821 and 1825 remained Pistrucci's close preserve. Wyon was responsible for the reverses of the copper coins.

The first sovereigns of George IV were sanctioned by Order in Council of 5th May 1821, in accordance with the submission made by Wellesley Pole on 10th April 1821. About this time Wellesley Pole was created an Irish peer and was thereafter known as Baron Maryborough. The submission stated:

'In further pursuance of your Majesty's Commands that Dies should be prepared for the Coining of Your Majesty's Monies I humbly beg leave to lay before Your Majesty a Design for the Gold Sovereign or Twenty Shilling piece having for the Obverse Impression the effigy of Your Majesty with the Inscription "Georgius IIII D.G. Britanniar Rex F.D." and for the Reverse the Image of St George, armed, sitting on horseback, attacking the Dragon with a Sword having broken his Spear in the Encounter, and the date of the Year. The edge of the piece is intended to be marked with the new invented Graining used on Coins of His late Majesty.'

Pistrucci was responsible for engraving the dies of both sides, but it is not known why the reverse motif was modified. In addition to the change of weapon, there are several other alterations to details of the design - notably St George's helmet, which was now shorn of its flowing streamer. The Dragon itself was substantially modified. The chief difference between the new sovereign and its predecessor, however, lay in the omission of the Garter and motto, their place being taken by a reeded border, and the transfer of the date from the obverse to the exergue of the reverse. Pistrucci's initials now appeared much more prominently in the exergue, to the right of the date.

The obverse bore a left-facing laureate head of George IV and, again, Pistrucci's initials appeared in the field, clear of the truncation. The lettering was reduced considerably and was now much better proportioned. This permitted the head to be substantially enlarged, and Pistrucci contrived to give the King an uncanny resemblance to the Roman Emperor Nero - gross features topped with a riot of curls, crowned with laurels in the Roman Imperial fashion.

The laureate sovereigns were minted annually from 1821 to 1825 but, despite the very substantial mintages in the first two years, they are difficult to find in the better grades of condition. Only 616,770 sovereigns were struck in 1823, but

Page 19: Two men were executed for making this false punch for sovereigns of George IV.

Two men named Buckle & Andrews were arrested while working on this punch and were afterwards executed. There was the last execution for forgery.

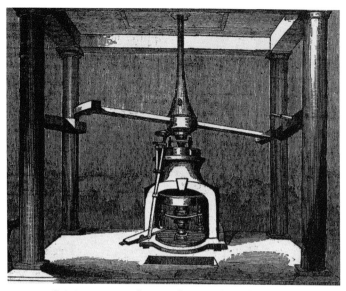

Coining press in the Royal Mint of London, 1836.

the vast majority appear to have been melted down as this is now rated as extremely rare. The majority of the specimens that have passed through the salerooms in the past twenty years have been in only fair to very fine condition. The 1825 date of this type is marginally more plentiful, and turns up from time to time in very fine-extremely fine condition.

George IV had wanted the obverse of the double sovereign of 1823 to show a bust sculpted by Francis Chantrey but Pistrucci refused to copy another artist's work. This was not the first time he had so refused. When Prince Regent, George IV had sent a portrait of himself by Sir Thomas Lawrence to Pistrucci to be used on the Waterloo medal and the sovereign. Pistrucci refused to copy Lawrence's work and, after many heated arguments, managed to get several sittings with the Prince Regent to produce his own image. Although Pistrucci reconsidered when Merlen agreed to copy the Chantrey bust, this second refusal gave Lord Maryborough, who had by now had enough of Latin temperament, a golden opportunity to be rid of the prima donna.

'The conduct of Mr Pistrucci in refusing to execute the order of the Master, in fulfillment of the King's command, renders him no longer of use to the Mint as Chief Engraver, whose peculiar duty it is to prepare the Head Dies for the Coin.' And it is probable he would not have continued in the Mint had not Lord Maryborough found it necessary to retain his services for completion of the Waterloo Medal.

The Waterloo Medal was, in fact, the ace which Pistrucci had up his sleeve. This was one of the most grandiose medallic projects ever contemplated, and was intended for presentation to the Allied heads of state and the victorious generals from the Battle of 1815 that had finally toppled Napoleon. Pistrucci worked on this elaborate medal for more than thirty years, latterly using it as a bargaining factor to ensure his continued employment. It is incredible that Pistrucci managed to spin out this work over so much time, and received such a large sum in payment. By the time the work was completed all of the intended recipients (except the Duke of Wellington) were dead, and the dies were anyway too large to be practicable in striking.

In June 1824 William Wyon was put in charge of die engraving. Pistrucci ceased to be employed on the engraving of coinage dies thereafter, although he continued to draw the inflated salary granted to him when he had taken the appointment in all but name. The true position was formally recognized by Royal Warrant of 15th January 1828, when Wyon was appointed Chief Engraver with an annual salary of £350 back-dated to 30th June 1827. Pistrucci's face was saved, however, as he was given a new post as Chief Medallist with the same salary of £350 a year. William Wyon produced excellent obverse dies based on the Chantrey bust and these were used for the sovereigns struck from 1825 to 1830. This neater, bare-headed profile was allied to a much shorter inscription GEORGIUS IV DEI GRATIA, the date being restored to the obverse.

For the reverse, an entirely new design was produced by Merlen which showed a garnished heraldic shield surmounted by a crown. This armorial design was to be used for the entire series of gold and the majority of silver coins, and in consideration of the work Merlen's salary was raised to £6 6s a week from 27th March 1824. Merlen's design, as used on the

George IV, large bare head two pounds, 1823.

George IV, bare head sovereign, 1828
Below: Reverse of a George IV laureate head sovereign showing St George and Dragon.

two years that the Gold Coinage Fund ran, £3,600,000 was coined for people other than the Bank of England; nearly the whole was for Messrs Rothschilds, with the balance being shared by a few large brokers. On the basis that the facilities had been meant to help smaller dealers, the fund was wound up and the original loan was repaid to Army funds, leaving the Mint with a small profit from interest and the cruder market way of assessing gold. From that moment, to by-pass the Bank was unprofitable and rare. Messrs Sharp, having had £19,256 coined in 1837, lamented that the loss of interest for 36 days exceeded the benefit of the direct approach by £25; £44 was gained and £69 was lost. Later, a well publicised private tender of gold to the Mint consisted of a single, small ingot sent in 1871 by Col. Tomline MP, to be coined into 100 sovereigns.

sovereign, was officially described as 'The Ensigns Armorial of the United Kingdom contained in a Shield, plain, surmounted by the Royal Crown'. The reverse legend continued the King's titles from the obverse, and was more fully inscribed BRITANNIARUM REX FID: DEF:.

The shield-back sovereigns of 1825-30 are not easy to find in the better grades of condition, despite the substantial mintage figures for most years. The figure of 4,200,343 for 1825 includes the earlier laureate sovereigns of that year. In 1828 only 386,182 were struck and these were chiefly from 1827 dies. Proof versions were struck in 1826. Counterfeits dated 1822, 1827 and 1828 exist; the latter are particularly troublesome, on account of the high premium paid for genuine sovereigns of that date.

Between 17th February 1829 and 1st March 1831, the Mint used an Army loan to buy gold and strike a stock of sovereigns, known as the Gold Coinage Fund. This fund was used to pay 'private' owners of bullion three-quarters of the coin due as soon as their consignment was weighed, with the balance due when the assays were reported, so they no longer had to stand the wait for coinage to be minted. During the

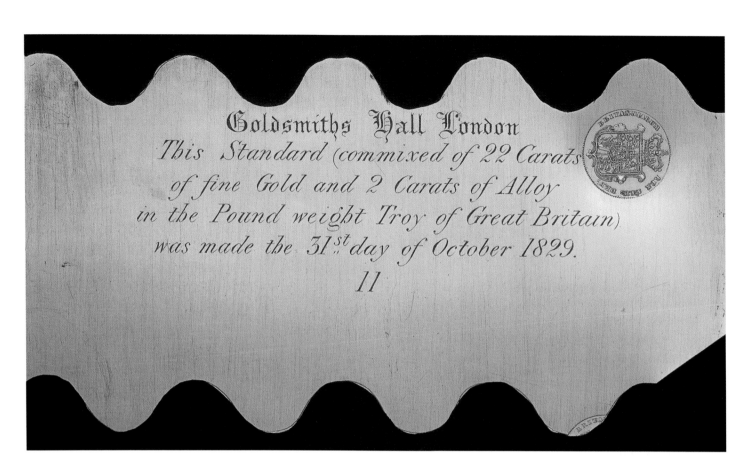

Goldsmiths Hall London
This Standard (commixed of 22 Carats
of fine Gold and 2 Carats of Alloy
in the Pound weight Troy of Great Britain)
was made the 31ˢᵗ day of October 1829.
11

King William IV
1830-1837

King William IV succeeded his brother on 26th June 1830, but almost five months elapsed before an order was formulated for the new coinage. J.C. Herries, the Master of the Mint, reported the situation on 15th November:

'The delay which has occurred in presenting the Memorial since His Majesty's commands were issued, although not beyond the usual period, has arisen in consequence of the difficulty and anxious desire to obtain an accurate and approved resemblance of His Majesty who was pleased to command that the effigy on his coins should be taken from the Bust which was executing at that time by Mr Chantrey.

Actual Size

Left above: The fineness of gold was checked against official trial plates A new gold trial plate, prepared in 1829, replaced the exhausted plate of 1688.

Left below: This pair of dies for William IV sovereigns of 1837, having struck 70,100 coins, was saved for the Royal Mint Museum.

'For this purpose it was desirable that a model should be prepared by Mr Chantrey adapted to the style used on the Coinage before Mr Wyon could be set to work: this of course occupied some time in addition to the time required by Mr Wyon for engraving the Dies on Steel (always a work of much labour) and the more so on this occasion when it was necessary to be done under the immediate personal superintendence and instruction of Mr Chantrey.'

In point of fact the dies were completed by Wyon no later than 28th October 1830, for Mr Herries was able to report to the Mint Board on that date that Wyon's design would be used for all coins, whether of gold, silver or copper. A bare-headed profile of the King, facing right, had Wyon's initials W.W. engraved on the truncation of the neck. The King's name and titles were rendered as GULIELMUS IIII D:G: BRITANNIAR: REX F:D: and the lettering was reduced in order to accommodate this long inscription on the obverse. On the other hand, the date was now transferred back to the reverse, for which Merlen was responsible.

The removal of the inscriptions from the reverse provided Merlen with greater scope in the interpretation of the crowned shield. The extravagant rococo scrollwork which garnished the shield was expanded, and the shield itself was broadened to take full advantage of the greater space. The quarterings, with the lions of England balanced by the lion rampant of Scotland and the Irish harp, were surmounted by the crowned shield of Hanover showing the armorial bearings of Brunswick, Luneberg and Celle. Though not as elaborate as the exquisite two-pound piece (which exists in proof form only), or the florid crown reverse, the sovereign was nevertheless a very handsome coin, marking the heraldic zenith of British numismatics.

The date appeared at the foot of the reverse. Rather than split the year into two pairs of digits flanking the heavily scrolled finial, the date in full was placed on the right and balanced by the Latin word ANNO (in the year). With the exception of 1834, sovereigns were struck annually in reasonable quantities from 1831 till 1837. A proof version was struck in 1831 for inclusion in the Coronation set of that year; only 598,547 sovereigns were struck in 1831 and this is undoubtedly the most elusive of the series and very rare. The 1835 coin is also rare, while the other dates, apart from 1832, are scarce. Some sovereigns dated 1832 have been counterfeited.

Queen Victoria
1837-1901

King William IV died without a legitimate child on 20th June 1837 and was succeeded by his eighteen-year-old niece Victoria, daughter of the late Duke of Kent. The kingdom of Hanover bowed to Salic Law, which forbade female succession, and thus the German dominions of the dynasty passed to Victoria's uncle, the unpopular and reactionary Duke of Cumberland. Satirical medalets, struck in brass the same size as the sovereign, parodied the St George and Dragon motif by showing the Duke of Cumberland on horseback, with the caption TO HANOVER round the top. These medalets, popularly known as 'Cumberland Jacks' or 'To Hanover' tokens, were subsequently much copied as gaming counters, and have survived in sufficient quantities to mystify and confuse collectors to this day.

The sovereigns of Queen Victoria, however, did not at first make use of Pistrucci's St George and Dragon motif. Like all the sovereigns since 1825, they had a crowned shield instead. The quarterings were now divested of the Hanoverian emblems and, as the shield was reduced in size, it was now wreathed in laurel. While the date was moved back to the obverse, the Queen's titles BRITANNIARUM REGINA FID: DEF: were transferred to the reverse. An already crowded reverse was further cluttered by the insertion of a nosegay of the heraldic flowers of the United Kingdom - thistle, rose and shamrock - below the knot of the wreath. This reverse was designed by Merlen, who was also credited with engraving the die.

An Order in Council, dated 26th July 1837, provided for the omission of the Hanoverian arms. On 22nd August, the Chancellor of the Exchequer wrote to the Master of the Mint:

'Her Majesty has commanded me to direct that the Chief Engraver and the Medallist of Her Majesty's Mint shall attend at Windsor Castle on Friday next for the purpose of having the advantage of study for their models in their respective departments. They should be at Windsor early and should report their arrival to the Lord or Groom in waiting. Her Majesty will give the artists separate sittings on Friday.'

Wyon prepared a wax model, which he subsequently used in engraving the obverse dies for the coinage. At this time Wyon's star was in the ascendant. He had been elected an Associate of the Royal Academy in 1831, and in 1838, when the new coinage appeared, he was elected a full member - the first medallist to receive this prestigious honour. In 1835 he had visited Lisbon and modelled the portrait of Queen Maria for the new Portuguese coinage, the dies for which he also engraved. In l836 he was elected an honorary member of the Imperial Academy of Fine Arts at Vienna.

It is idle to speculate whether Wyon and Pistrucci travelled together to Windsor but their rivalry was far from over, despite the fact that their roles were quite separate. From a letter by R.J. Lane to Richard Sainthill (a leading numismatist of the period) we learn that Wyon refused to take his sittings of the Queen with Pistrucci at work in the room. Sainthill, however, commented that 'Wyon was entirely free from any feeling of jealousy, as regarded other artists in his own profession, native or foreign, at every period of his life; nor was this disposition ever disturbed by the malevolence and injustice which, at some stages of his career, he encountered from others'. Pistrucci, on the other hand, complained loudly that Wyon had spoiled his dies for the Coronation Medal by retouching them. Ironically, Wyon is probably better remembered nowadays for his splendid crowned profile of the Queen, which he executed for the Guildhall Medal of 1837 and which served as the basis for all the British postage stamps until 1902. Lane observed that Wyon's Guildhall Medal was 'the most exquisitely perfect and true portrait of the Queen'.

On 15th February 1838 the Master of the Mint submitted to the Queen designs for the sovereign:

Left: A Post Office notice of 1837, urging the public to take special precautions when sending sovereigns through the post.
Right: A Victoria young head obverse with a shield and a St George and Dragon reverse.

'In pursuance of Your Majesty's gracious Command that Dies for your Majesty's Coins should be prepared according to the Model of an Effigy of your Majesty which I had the honour to submit for your Majesty's approbation and also new Reverses for the Gold and Silver Coinage.

'I humbly beg leave to lay before your Majesty the annexed specimen of the Impression intended to be struck on the Sovereign or 20 Shilling piece namely for the Obverse Impression the aforesaid Effigy of your Majesty with the inscription "Victoria Dei Gratia" and the date of the year. For the Reverse impression the Ensigns Armorial of the United Kingdom according to the Design approved by your Majesty in Council dated 26th July 1837 contained in a plain shield, surmounted by the Royal Crown and encircled with a Laurel Wreath, with the inscription "Britanniarum Regina Fid: Def:" having the united Rose, Thistle and Shamrock placed under the Shield.'

The designs were formally approved on 26th February 1838. The left-facing profile of the young Queen, her hair drawn back into a chignon and her head bound by a double fillet, made for a very graceful and elegant obverse, helped by the restrained use of lettering round the top, with the date below the truncation of the neck. Wyon's initials were placed on the truncation, towards the right.

For nigh on half a century, from 1838 till 1887, Wyon's young head obverse was used for the sovereign, giving this popular coin an ageless quality which doubtless helped to establish it as the leading bullion coin of the world in the nineteenth century. Merlen's crowned shield reverse was just as long-lived, as it continued to be used for some of the sovereigns struck at the branch mints (discussed in the next chapter). However, it ceased to be employed in London after 1874 and had been largely superseded from 1871 onwards by Pistrucci's St George and the Dragon. As the date appeared in the exergue of the St George type, a modified obverse was required. The Queen's profile was lowered so that the point of the truncation touched the rim, thus permitting the titles VICTORIA D:G: BRITANNIAR: REG: F:D: to be placed around the top.

*A pocket balance. In 1891, in the **House of Commons**, Sir William Harcourt recalled the time in his youth when shopkeepers produced a pair of scales and weighed the coins tendered by customers.*

The first type of sovereign, with the shield reverse, was regularly minted from 1838 till 1874, with the exception of 1840 and 1867. Most dates are fairly common, but many of them are surprisingly elusive in very fine, extremely fine and uncirculated grades. Sovereigns dated 1848-50 and 1858-60 are elusive and command a good premium, while the first Victorian sovereigns of all, dated 1838, are relatively rare and are much in demand as the first of the series. Very few sovereigns were struck in 1839 and 1841 so they are consequently rated very rare and extremely rare.

The young head sovereigns produced several very interesting and rare varieties. Two rare variants of 1838 and 1843 sovereigns are known as 'narrow shields' although this is something of a misnomer as the 1838 variety displays taller laurels and the 1843 more compact floral emblems. It should be noted that every die was liable to retouching where necessary, after it had been sunk from the punch. In 1848 William Wyon gave evidence before the Royal Mint Commission and said: 'with respect to the dies, every die is perfected by the graver, re-lettered etc., and in fact made an original before it is hardened; so that, in case of a failure of the original matrix, a die could be converted into and used as a matrix, so as to obtain puncheons from it'.

Proof versions of the sovereign were produced in 1839 and 1853 for inclusion in presentation sets: the 1839 sets were struck in the 1840s. The 1839 and 1853 proof sovereigns are major rarities.

Another variety is the so-called 'Ansell' sovereign of 1859. The normal sovereign of that date was minted in an edition of 1,547,603 but today is a scarce coin. In addition, however, some 167,539 sovereigns were struck from a consignment of gold that emanated from the gold fields of Australia. The gold, in its original state, was considered too brittle for coining purposes on account of certain impurities (antimony, lead and arsenic) which it contained. G.F. Ansell, a metallurgist employed by the Mint, conducted a series of experiments with this metal and reworked it satisfactorily into sovereigns, earning for himself a special letter of thanks and £100 from the Master of the Mint. These 'Ansell' sovereigns can be recognized by an additional line on the lower edge of the fillet at the nape of the Queen's neck. Later Thomas Graham, Master of the Mint, dismissed G.F. Ansell, essentially because of criticism aired by Ansell over changes introduced by Graham and his brother John.

Changes at the Mint

Following Merlen's retirement, William Wyon's son, Leonard Charles, was appointed Second Engraver on 23rd July 1844. William Wyon died in 1851 and his son became in effect, but not in title, the non-resident Chief Engraver. At the same time James Wyon, a cousin of Leonard Charles Wyon, became resident engraver. On his departure in 1860, his son George was appointed in his place, but he died in 1862. Leonard Charles Wyon continued as

Above: Minting processes at the end of the nineteenth century.
Left:Victoria young head type IA 'Ansell' sovereign 1859, identified with an additional raised line on the lower part of the ribbon (M42A).

Engraver till his death in 1891. Although this brought to an end the remarkable record of service of the Wyon family, it should be noted that subsequent generations of Wyons have continued to work as medallists and die engravers.

In 1851 the Mint was the subject of sweeping organisational reforms. The new Master of the Mint, Sir John Herschel, was determined to improve the weight and fineness of coins to standards that had not been achieved in previous years. There was even public criticism suggesting that Russian gold was more reliable than the sovereign. Sir John Herschel achieved his goal: modern assays show that 1851 was indeed a turning point - the fineness of coins dated 1838-1851 was 915.31, while coins dated 1852-1873 was 916.30.

In 1863 tiny die numbers were added to the reverse between the knot of the wreath and the heraldic flowers. Die numbers were introduced to give a definite identification of the die itself, and to enable badly struck coins to be traced back to the operator responsible. Plate numbers were first

engraved on postage stamps about the same time; they were intended as a security feature and a precaution against forgery, so it may be that the die numbers on the sovereigns had the additional purpose of security.

Sovereigns minted in 1863 exist with or without die numbers, the latter being only marginally less common. Thereafter, all the sovereigns of the first type down to 1874 had die numbers on the reverse, except for 1872, when quite a considerable number were struck without die numbers in addition to those that bore this feature.

The numerical sequence started afresh at the beginning of each year, when the date on the obverse was changed. Numbers from 1 to 123 have been recorded, but there are many gaps in the sequence. Either certain dies were never employed, or sovereigns that were actually struck have yet to be recorded with the missing numbers.

Interestingly, the first year of die numbers also gave rise to another variety. This is the exceedingly rare sovereign with the tiny numerals 827 replacing Wyon's initials in the truncation of the neck on the obverse. The first example of this coin came to light as recently as October 1954, being discovered in a large accumulation of sovereigns by F.H. Pugh at Hatton, Derbyshire. This coin had the die number 22 on the reverse. A second example turned up in Sri Lanka in 1975. The following year a third coin was discovered, but this lacked the die number. A fourth example, also with a numberless reverse, was acquired by Spink & Son early in 1977. A fifth specimen, with die number 22, was discovered in 1979 and Michael Marsh, author of *The Gold Sovereign*, found a sixth example. More recent auctions have contained both varieties.

Various theories have been propounded regarding the mysterious numerals. The Mint records indicate that experiments were carried out in 1863 using gold ingots numbered 816 and 830, and from this Graham Dyer, Librarian and Curator of the Royal Mint, deduced that the 827 referred to an ingot used in the striking. These ingots weighed 200 ounces, so that the total number of sovereigns that could have been struck from this particular ingot would never have amounted to more than a few hundreds. It is significant that several examples should have been discovered in recent years as the existence of this variety has become more widely publicized, but it is unlikely that many more will ever come to light.

Die numbers were not used in connection with the sovereigns with the modified obverse and St George reverse.

M26

M125

M84A

M149

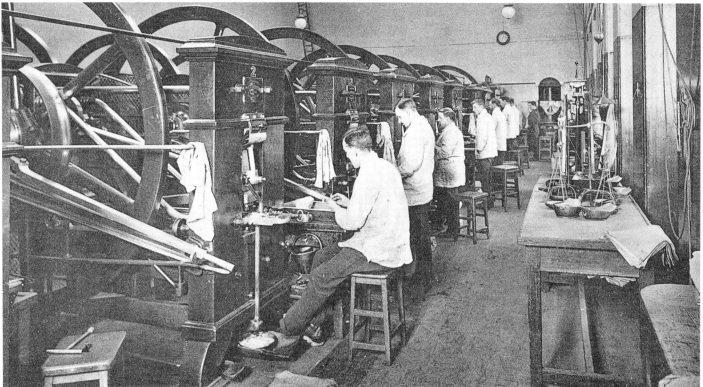

Left: The four heads of Victoria: young head type I (M26), young head type II (M84A), jubilee issue (M125) and old head (M149).
Above: Minting processes at the end of the nineteenth century.

This type was adopted in 1871 and struck regularly in great abundance till 1874, and in 1876, 1878-80 and 1884-5 thereafter. All of these dates are commoner than the preceding type, apart from 1878, which is on a par with the commoner sovereigns of the shield-back type, and 1879 which is a rare coin and generally rates five or six times as much as the more abundant dates of this type.

From the 1850s production of sovereigns was established at the branch mints in Australia to exploit the gold discovered in New South Wales and Victoria, and later in Western Australia. These mints and their output of sovereigns are discussed in the next chapter.

A New Image of Victoria

After half a century of seeing Queen Victoria immortalised on coinage as a teenager, it must have come as a shock to the public when her portrait was updated to mark her Golden Jubilee in 1887 - by which time the Queen was a 68-year-old widow. The new obverse was modelled in plaster by Sir Joseph Edgar Boehm, and showed a matronly bust of the ageing Queen wearing an absurd little crown atop her widow's veil. Not the most sympathetic bust of Victoria even when seen on

the larger coins, such as the crown and double-florin, it lost much of its charm by the time it was reduced to fit the dimensions of the sovereign, which tended to emphasise the heavy jowls, beaky nose and receding chin, without any redeeming features. Victoria was shown wearing the ribbon and star of the Garter and the family order of Victoria and Albert.

The extent of the bust and height of the crown meant that the lettering had to be confined to the sides of the obverse: VICTORIA D: G: on one side and BRITT: REG: F: D: on the other. By contrast, Pistrucci's St George and Dragon was now so well entrenched in public esteem that it was retained for the reverse. Indeed, the flowing streamer that had been removed from St George's helmet in 1821 was now restored. Both obverse and reverse dies for the sovereign were supervised by Leonard Charles Wyon, although the application of the reducing machine must have made the preparation of steel dies from the original plasters a lot more mechanical than in the old days of hand engraving. Nevertheless, it is the initials of Boehm and Pistrucci that appear on the obverse and reverse of the Jubilee sovereign.

Sovereigns without a mintmark were struck at London annually from 1887 till 1892, and rank among the commonest of all bullion coins, although the 1888 sovereigns are scarce in the finer grades of condition and the 1887 sovereign rates a premium as the first of the series. 1887 Jubilee London mint sovereigns appear as a very yellow gold which was due to an addition of approximately 1.25% silver to make the gold softer to facilitate the striking of the new portrait.

In February 1891 the Chancellor of the Exchequer, George Goschen, requested a committee to consider and report on the designs used for coinage. The committee, under the chairmanship of Sir John

The success and popularity of the gold sovereign has always been dependent upon the accuracy of the Royal Mint.

Lubbock, Liberal MP, banker, archaeologist and naturalist, was made up of David Powell, Deputy Governor of the Bank of England; Richard Blaney Wade, Chairman of the National Provincial Bank; Sir Frederic Leighton, President of the Royal Academy; Sir John Evans, President of the Numismatic Society; and Charles Fremantle, representing the Royal Mint. The secretary was George F. Glennie, Deputy Secretary of the Bank of England. The committee agreed that eight artists would submit two portraits of Queen Victoria: the prospective artists were A. Gilbert; E. O. Ford; E. J. Poynter; H. Thornycroft; H. Armstead; C. B. Birch; T. Brock; and T. Woolner – all members and associate members of the Royal Academy. On the 27th November 1892 the committee recommended that designs by Thomas Brock and Edward Poynter should be used.

Brock's old head obverse was introduced in 1893 and showed the veiled crowned bust of Victoria wearing the ribbon and star of the Garter with the initials T.B. below the bust. The opportunity was taken to change the titles on the obverse, which now read VICTORIA DEI GRA. BRITT. REGINA FID. DEF. IND. IMP. The last part of the inscription alluded to the Queen's title of Empress of India, assumed since 1876. Considerable ingenuity was shown in accommodating such a lengthy inscription on an obverse which had also to make allowance for the ample bosom of the Queen. Inevitably, the St George and Dragon reverse remained unchanged.

Sovereigns of this type were struck in vast quantities, even exceeding those of the preceding series. This was due to the institution of a policy of continuous recoinage, with worn coins being automatically removed from circulation by the Bank of England and replaced by coins of full weight. New coins were also required to replace those unofficially melted down by jewellers and dentists. Sovereigns were issued annually from 1893 to 1901, while proofs were included in the sets minted in the inaugural year.

Accurate weights were essential at all stages of the minting process. Much also depended on the judgement of the tryer, who was responsible for ensuring that blanks of correct weight were cut from the rolled strips of gold.

King Edward VII
1901-1910

King George V
1910-1936

Queen Victoria died at Osborne, Isle of Wight, on 22nd January 1901. An Austrian sculptor, Emil Fuchs, was called in to take a cast of the dead Queen's features for a death mask. This rather macabre incident brought Fuchs to the notice of Edward VII, who was impressed by his work and sat for a portrait that was used by Fuchs in the design of the postage stamps. A maquette of the Fuchs bare-headed profile of the King was subsequently used by George William De Saulles, who modelled the effigy used for the coinage. The obverse shows the King facing right, with the initials De S engraved below the truncation of the neck. The inscription was now expanded even further and included the abbreviation BRITT: OMN: - 'all the Britains' - to signify the far-flung British Empire. This was underlined in a practical manner, for in addition to the branch mints in Melbourne, Sydney and Perth, a mint was opened in Ottawa to process Canadian gold from the Klondike.

Pistrucci's St George and Dragon remained serene as ever on the reverse. The output of sovereigns at London attained new heights, as the demand for British gold in the world's bullion markets increased. Proof sovereigns were produced for inclusion in the Coronation set of 1902. Unlike previous issues, however, these had a matt finish. Sovereigns were struck each year from 1902 till 1910 in great profusion. All of these Edwardian sovereigns are uniformly common and there is no variation in value.

The Australian sculptor, Bertram Mackennal, ARA, designed the left-facing profile of George V used for the coinage introduced in 1911. He had settled in London and came to prominence in 1908, when he was responsible for designing the medals awarded at the Olympic Games. Mackennal prepared a preliminary maquette from photographs of the King taken by W. & D. Downey Limited, and completed his work from a special sitting granted by the King. From the plaster medallion, master punches of coinage dimension were cut by means of a reducing machine. Mackennal's initials appear on the truncation. Apart from substituting the name of the new monarch, the titles on the obverse remained the same.

Normal production of sovereigns in London was confined to the first five years of the reign and dates from 1911 to 1915 are very common. After the outbreak of the First World War in August 1914, however, gold was withdrawn from circulation in the United Kingdom itself, although sovereigns continued to be minted for bullion transactions and, increasingly, the 'sinews of war'. Production at London continued till 1917, over 1.5 million being struck in 1916 and just over a million the following year. The Treasury notes, which had been introduced on the outbreak of war, were theoretically fully convertible, but the public was requested to refrain from asking for gold. As the currency remained stable the notes soon won acceptance, and gold in general circulation became a thing of the past.

It seems unlikely that the sovereigns of 1916 and 1917 passed into the hands of the general public. Instead, they were earmarked for the Bank of England gold reserve, from which substantial quantities were exported to the United States to cover purchases of munitions and war material in America. They undoubtedly found their way to Fort Knox, where they remained until 1934. In that year the United States Gold Reserve Act required that all gold coin owned by the Federal government had to be melted and converted to bars. Thus the vast majority of the sovereigns struck in 1916 and 1917 - not to mention the untold hoards of earlier sovereigns which must have been in Fort Knox at that time - were destroyed in this operation. The 1916 sovereign is a very scarce coin, while 1917 is extremely rare, making it one of the greatest rarities in the entire series.

After the First World War, paper money continued to take the place of gold and it was not until 1925 that production of sovereigns was briefly resumed at the Royal Mint in London, though the branch mints had been very active in the interim. Under the Gold Standard Act of 1925, bank notes and Treasury notes ceased to be convertible on demand into coin - although the Bank of England was obliged to sell 400-ounce bars of fine gold to anyone who asked for it and paid the purchase price of £3 17s 10d per ounce standard in legal tender. Between 1929 and 1930 the demand for these gold bars forced the Royal Mint to melt down 91,350,000 sovereigns from the stock held by the Bank of England. Indubitably further demands of this nature continued to deplete the holdings of sovereigns from time to time, which is why extant quantities bear little or no resemblance to the original mintage figures.

Many of the sovereigns actually struck in 1925 were consigned to the melting pot, which explains why they were very rare for a number of years. Fortunately the Royal Mint retained the dies for 1925 and produced almost a million 1925 sovereigns between 1949 and 1952, due to demand on the international bullion markets. The later pieces had the appearance of being thicker than the original issue because of a more pronounced rim.

A 1904 gold sovereign is to be found in the base of the rod of office of the Gentleman Usher of the Black Rod.

Death-knell for the Sovereign

The worldwide economic crisis of 1931, triggered by the collapse of the Credit-Anstalt Bank of Austria, resulted in Britain abandoning the Gold Standard and seemed to sound the death-knell for the sovereign. Production at the various branch mints throughout the Empire then ceased and, although gold coins continued to be freely traded in bullion deals, none was struck in the 1930s for general circulation.

The only sovereigns contemplated were the proofs intended for inclusion in the Coronation set of King Edward VIII in 1937 – these were prepared but never issued, although a few examples are known to exist. These proof sovereigns bear the initials of Humphrey Paget below the truncation of the King's neck. Proof sovereigns with the left-facing profile of King George VI, designed by Paget, were included in the Coronation set of 1937. To emphasise that they were not intended for general circulation they were struck without milling on the edge.

Queen Elizabeth II
1952-

The position regarding proof sovereigns at the commencement of the present reign was even more restricted than it had been in 1937. Proofs were certainly produced, using the right-facing profile of the Queen by Mary Gillick, but none was ever made available to collectors at the time of issue in 1953. These sovereigns, intended solely for various national collections, differed from their predecessors in omitting the legend IND. IMP., the Indian Empire having been granted independence in 1947.

Primarily to satisfy the demands of the bullion market the minting of sovereigns was resumed in 1957, with a finer milled edge to combat counterfeiting. These coins continued to bear the Gillick obverse, but now the words BRITT. OMN. were dropped from the inscription, reflecting the 'wind of change' sweeping through the British Commonwealth at that time. When sovereigns were struck in 1958, a rather coarser milling on the edge was adopted and this was employed for subsequent issues. With the exception of 1960-1, sovereigns were issued in abundance from 1957 to 1968 and rate little more than the prevailing bullion price.

The operation of the Gold Exchange Control Order by the Labour government brought the production of sovereigns to a halt once more, and it was not until this legislation was repealed by the Conservative government in 1973 that resumption of gold coins could be contemplated. Ironically, Labour had returned to power by the time the first sovereigns of 1974 were becoming available and renewed restrictions made their holding by UK residents very difficult. These restrictions were finally rescinded by the Thatcher government in 1979.

Production of sovereigns for the international bullion market continued, however, and coins dated 1976 and from 1978 to 1982 were later made freely available and trade to this day at their bullion value. The Royal Mint, now increasingly aware of the collector market, began striking annual proof versions in 1979, and this policy has continued to the present time.

In 1974 the tiara profile of the Queen by Arnold Machin, RA, was adopted for the obverse, but Pistrucci's St George and Dragon continued to appear on the reverse. Machin sovereigns were struck in 1974, 1976 and from 1978 till 1982, proof versions being struck in addition to the circulating coins from 1979 onwards. The more mature profile of the Queen, wearing a diadem, was designed by Raphael David Maklouf and introduced in 1985. 1998 saw the introduction of a matronly profile of the Queen wearing a tiara designed by Ian Rank-Broadley. Since 1983, however, with the exception of the year 2000, sovereigns have only been struck in proof versions for sale to collectors, and it seems probable that the bullion role of the sovereign is now being taken over by the new Britannia coinage based on the ounce troy.

A one-off change in sovereign design, the first for over a century and a half, was unveiled in January 1989. A set of four coins, comprising half-sovereign, sovereign, £2 and £5, was issued in proof form later in the year to mark the 500th anniversary of the introduction of the gold sovereign by King Henry VII in 1489. The designs were modelled by Bernard Sindall on the Tudor sovereign, but were subtly brought up to date. Thus the obverse portrays Queen Elizabeth full length, seated on the Coronation chair in Westminster Abbey, in full Coronation regalia. This motif, in fact, was derived from a medal struck by the Royal Mint in 1977 to celebrate the Queen's Silver Jubilee. The reverse shows a plain spade-shaped shield bearing the royal arms, superimposed on a double Tudor rose surmounted by a Tudor single-arched crown. The obverse legend reads ELIZABETH II DEI GRA. REG. FID. DEF. in medieval Lombardic script. Similar lettering was used for the reverse inscription ANNIVERSARY OF THE GOLD SOVEREIGN 1489-1989. This was the first commemorative sovereign to be issued in Britain.

Above left: Obverse of a decimal Elizabeth II third issue sovereign (M312).
Above right: Obverse of an Elizabeth II fourth issue proof sovereign (M328).
Far left: George V, small head sovereign, 1932, mintmark SA (Pretoria) (M296).

A group of early Sydney sovereigns, from a hoard discovered in the United Kingdom some forty years ago.

THE BRANCH MINTS

A unique aspect of sovereign production was the establishment of several branches of the Royal Mint outside the British Isles. No other country since the fall of the Roman Empire had spread its coin production over such a vast area. In this case, policy was dictated by the enormous distances involved in the far-flung British Empire. When gold was discovered in New South Wales and Victoria in the mid-nineteenth century, it seemed eminently sensible to refine and assay the gold on the spot and from that it was but a short step to the conversion of that gold into a convenient form in the shape of sovereigns.

Reverse of a Victoria
young head type I sovereign with Sydney mintmark.

Australia

Gold was discovered in workable quantities in the eastern part of New South Wales in 1851, and in the neighbouring colony of Victoria soon afterwards. Almost immediately, the colonial authorities petitioned the home government for the establishment of minting facilities in their territories. Sydney, Melbourne and Adelaide all put in their claims to be the venue of the proposed Australian mint. The Government Assay Office in Adelaide, in fact, jumped the gun by striking gold pieces tariffed at £1 in 1852. These pieces were in the fineness and weight of the British sovereign. The obverse showed a royal crown above the date and had the name of the issuing authority round the circumference. The reverse was inscribed VALUE ONE POUND in the centre. Round the top the weight was given (5dwt 15grs) and round the foot was the fineness - 22 carats. Two different types of the Adelaide pound were struck in 1852, but the issue was short-lived and examples are now very rare.

Sydney Mint

Sydney had an association with minting, which went back to the early years of the penal colony at Botany Bay. In 1813 Governor Macquarie had imported Spanish silver dollars and converted each piece, worth 5 shillings, into two separate coins totalling 6s 3d in local currency. He achieved this miracle by having the centres cut out. The rings were countermarked and passed current at 5 shillings, but the centres, or 'dumps', were stamped 15 pence. These Holey Dollars and Dumps continued in use until 1826, when the Sterling Silver Money Act did away with the need for them. These emergency coins were struck in Sydney from dies engraved by a convict named William Henshall, who had been transported to Botany Bay for counterfeiting.

The legislation enabling the establishment of the Sydney branch mint passed through the British Parliament in August 1853, and it was officially opened in the south wing of the old Rum Hospital on 14th May 1855. The first coins were struck on 23rd June of that year.

As soon as the necessary Act was passed, the contract for minting equipment and machinery was awarded to Joseph Taylor of Birmingham; Ralph Heaton of the Birmingham Mint stood surety for the contract. Two lever presses were despatched to Sydney and installed in a room at the rear of the hospital and the dies for sovereigns and half-sovereigns were supplied by the Royal Mint and engraved by James Wyon, son of George Wyon. The British Government required the coins to be different from those minted in England. The obverse was not unlike that engraved by William Wyon for the British gold coins, but the Queen's name and titles were all inscribed round the circumference, with the date below the truncation of the neck.

This freed the reverse for a design that was quite unlike anything used in Britain itself. The principal motif consisted of a flat-arched crown above the word AUSTRALIA in a wreath, with SYDNEY MINT at the top and ONE (or HALF) SOVEREIGN at the foot. Thus these coins broke with tradition in several respects: they bore an actual notation of value; they included the name of the mint and, most important of all, they were inscribed with a name which did not become a political entity for almost half a century - for it was not until 1901 that the six colonies came together to form the Commonwealth of Australia.

Leonard Charles Wyon, best remembered for engraving the dies for the British bronze coinage, was responsible for a new obverse, introduced in 1857, showing a more mature profile of Queen Victoria. It had been decided that the obverse should have a more distinctly Australian flavour, and for this reason the Queen was portrayed with a different hairstyle and a spray of Banksia forming her diadem. These sovereigns appeared annually till 1870, though none was produced for general circulation dated 1869. Originally, these

The Sydney branch mint. The building had begun life in 1811 as the south wing of Governor Macquarie's Rum Hospital, built by contractors in return for the right to purchase and import 45,000 gallons of rum into the colony.

coins were supposed to circulate in New South Wales, but the British Treasury later amended the ordinance to include 'and other colonies of Australasia'.

This only served to annoy Adelaide and Melbourne, both of which petitioned the Imperial Government for their own mints. When their requests were ignored, they circulated a rumour that the Sydney gold coins were inferior in quality to their British counterparts. Some merchants in the colony of Victoria added insult to injury by giving only 19 shillings for Sydney sovereigns. In January 1856 the home authorities acted by making a snap check of Sydney sovereigns. It was then discovered that the New South Wales coins had a higher intrinsic worth than the British coins, mainly because the gold was alloyed with silver as well as copper. Now the word spread and the 'good' sovereigns rapidly disappeared from circulation as merchants melted them down for their intrinsic value.

Fortunately, the Sydney Mint could cope with the demand and continued to strike sovereigns as long as they were required. Production rose from 1,101,000 in 1858 to 2,911,000 in 1866. Australian sovereigns even circulated unofficially in Britain, and they were accepted without question as far afield as Newfoundland. The position was eventually regularised by a Royal Proclamation of 3rd February 1866, in the aftermath of the Colonial Branch Mint Act of that year, which declared the Sydney coins to be a legal tender for payment within the United Kingdom. They were also adopted as legal tender by an increasing number of countries, particularly India, using them as bullion coins. Indians preferred Australian sovereigns because they were of a yellow colour, rather than the redder colour of London.

This success, however, was their very undoing. It was subsequently decided that only one type of sovereign should be struck in the Mint and its branches. In 1870 the distinctive Australian obverse and reverse were abolished and the standard British types were adopted instead. However, the branch mints could choose to strike the St George and Dragon reverse by Pistrucci, or the shield reverse. India's preference was for the shield, and by public demand Sydney - and later Melbourne - continued to strike the shield type long after London had stopped.

The mintmark S appeared on the armorial reverse, between the heraldic flowers and the knot of the wreath; on the St George and Dragon coins, the mintmark was shifted to the obverse and appeared below the truncation. Both designs

Actual Size

Reverse of a Victoria old head sovereign with Perth mintmark (M173).
Reverse of an Edward VII Canadian mint (Ottawa) sovereign (M184).
Reverse of an Edward VII sovereign with Melbourne mintmark (M191).
Reverse of a George V Indian mint (Bombay) sovereign (M228).

were used for sovereigns struck regularly each year in considerable quantities until 1887, but only the shield-back sovereigns dated 1871 and 1875 can be regarded as common nowadays. At the other extreme, the sovereigns dated 1881 and 1887 are both particularly scarce and other dates, such as 1878 and 1883, are difficult to find in the better grades.

The St George sovereigns in general are more plentiful, though those dated 1871, with either normal or large B.P. initials, are rare; these varieties with initials also occur in other dates.

Melbourne Mint

At long last the colonial government of Victoria had their way and a branch of the Royal Mint was established in Melbourne on 12th June 1872. It began striking sovereigns that year, using the letter M as a mintmark. Shield sovereigns were minted in 1872, 1874 and continuously from 1880 to 1887. For many years there was an unsubstantiated rumour that shield sovereigns were also struck in 1875, but the records of the Royal Mint show that no dies for such a date were manufactured. This series, however, has yielded some of the greatest rarities among Australian sovereigns, those dated 1880, 1883, 1886 and 1887 being particularly rare.

The Melbourne St George sovereigns with young head obverse were struck annually from 1872 till 1887. The coins dated 1881 yield three distinct varieties: with normal B.P.; large B.P.; or omitting B.P. altogether - the latter two variants being rated scarce and rare respectively. Sovereigns dated 1872 and 1876, as well as the large B.P. varieties of 1882 and 1887, are scarce.

Jubilee sovereigns were struck at both Sydney and Melbourne from 1887 to 1893. The first and last dates from Melbourne are scarce, but the others are normal. Of the Sydney sovereigns, only 1887 is rare, 1889 is common and the rest are normal.

The Melbourne branch mint. Specially constructed for the purpose and opened on 12 June 1872, the mint was later described as one of the six best buildings in Melbourne.

Both branch mints struck old head sovereigns from 1893 till 1901. The Melbourne coins are plentiful - as are those from Sydney, apart from 1896, which is scarce.

After the discovery of large deposits of gold in Kalgoorlie and Coolgardie, Western Australia in 1898, a third branch mint was established in Perth on 20th June 1899. Only 690,992 sovereigns were struck with the P mintmark in 1899 and today these are regarded as scarce. Output was accelerated in 1900 and 1901 and both dates rank as normal.

Coins from the three Australian branch mints made up around 40% of the total of sovereigns circulating within Britain during the first decade of the twentieth century; as far as daily use was concerned, they were indistinguishable from those sovereigns issued directly from the Mint in London. The Australian branch mints struck Edwardian sovereigns from 1902 to 1910 in vast quantities. All of them are common, except the Sydney sovereigns of 1908-10, which are rated as normal. There are also great rarities of the 1920s from the Melbourne and Sydney mints.

The Mackennal profile of George V, as in London, was used on the sovereigns struck at the branch mints. In 1927, however, the Royal Mint introduced a new obverse for silver coins and extended it to bronze coins the following year. In this the head was slightly reduced, producing a more balanced design. The small head obverse was adopted for the sovereign in 1929 and was used in the last three years of the Perth and Melbourne sovereigns and the final four years of the South African coins.

Canada

In 1858 gold was discovered in the Fraser Valley, British Columbia. Captain Driscoll Gossett was appointed colonial treasurer and arrived at Victoria on Vancouver Island later that year, armed with authority to establish a mint if necessary, and mindful of the precedent set in Australia. Gossett, however, persuaded the colonial governor that the mint should be located at New Westminster, on the mainland of British Columbia, to take advantage of the gold strikes in that vicinity. A coining press was acquired and gold $20 pieces were struck as samples and sent to the International Exhibition in London in 1862.

Unfortunately, the original gold deposits were quickly worked out, and by 1871 the New Westminster mint and assay office had closed down. At this time Canada obtained its coinage from the Royal Mint in London or from the Heaton Mint in Birmingham. The federal government was perfectly satisfied with this arrangement, but from time to time various politicians raised the matter in Parliament. Agitation for a Canadian mint was whipped up in 1897-8, following the first discovery of vast quantities of gold in the Klondike.

Previously it was felt that the cost of establishing a Canadian mint would not be justified by the relatively small amount of coinage required for everyday use; the major gold strikes at the turn of the century put a different complexion on the matter. Following Australian precedent, it seemed feasible that the home government would shoulder the burden of costs if such a mint were established as a branch of the Royal Mint for the specific purpose of coining British sovereigns from Canadian gold. The Canadian government would have liked the sovereigns to be inscribed CANADIAN MINT, but this was rejected by the home authorities.

Eventually a branch mint was established in Ottawa on 2nd January 1908. Its purpose was two-fold: to manufacture the silver and bronze coins for everyday circulation, and to mint sovereigns from Canadian gold. The latter were produced from dies supplied by the Royal Mint and had the mintmark C above the date on the reverse. Only 636 sovereigns were struck in 1908 and barely a handful has survived, making this one of the outstanding rarities of the entire sovereign series. Some 16,273 sovereigns were struck in 1909 and 28,012 in 1910, and today both of these coins are rare.

All six branch mints struck sovereigns with the effigy of George V on the obverse. Sovereigns were struck at Ottawa in 1911, 1913, 1914, and from 1916 to 1919, but all of them are difficult to find. Those dated 1911, 1918 and 1919 are scarce and the others are rare. Only 6,119 sovereigns were struck in 1916, with only a dozen or so now in private hands, while the 1913 sovereign is also very rare.

The Perth branch, decorated with patriotic fervour for the royal visit on 24 July 1901 of Their Royal Highnesses the Duke and Duchess of York.

India

The Bombay Mint, dating from 1672, is one of the oldest mints in Asia and produced coins for the East India Company and later administrations down to the present day. A gold refinery was established in 1918, expressly for the purpose of refining the South African gold. During 1919 and 1920 almost two million tolas of gold was refined. In addition to imports from the Rand mines, a vast quantity of gold was brought to the mint as a result of a wartime measure known as the Gold Import Act. A suitable structure, designated as a branch of the Royal Mint in London, was erected in the Bombay Mint compound, but completely isolated from the mint, for the specific purpose of converting South African and recycled Indian gold into sovereigns. These were of the standard British pattern, with George V on the obverse and the St George and Dragon reverse, but the letter I (India) was inserted in the exergue line above the date. Some

Reverse of a George V South African mint (Pretoria) sovereign (M289).

1,296,033 sovereigns were struck before the branch operation closed in April 1919 for economic reasons. All of these sovereigns bore the date 1918 and are rated as normal.

The Ottawa branch, opened on 2 January 1908, was to strike less than one million sovereigns. Like the other branches, it was supplied with dies from London.

South Africa

In 1873 a Swiss assayer named Perrin came to the South African Republic (now known as the Transvaal) and had discussions with President Burgers about setting up a mint in Pretoria. The equipment was purchased by Perrin in Germany and shipped out to Africa, but was impounded by the Customs officials at Delagoa Bay in Portuguese East Africa until the necessary duty had been paid. When this was communicated to the Volksraad (the Republic's parliament), the Boers refused to pay up, so Perrin's expensive equipment was left to rust away at Delagoa Bay. The following year a contract was awarded to the Birmingham Mint, which struck the beautiful gold coins known as Burgersponds.

The discovery of gold at Witwatersrand, however, made a local mint imperative. A site was chosen and the foundation stone laid by Paul Kruger in July 1892. Proof sets appeared that year and circulating coinage from 1892 onwards. These coins conformed to the specifications laid down by the British Coinage Act of 1870, and included gold ponds following the size, weight and fineness of the sovereign. These coins portrayed President Kruger on the obverse and had the arms of the Republic on the reverse. The Pretoria Mint continued to strike republican coins till 1900. Ironically, by far the largest output of gold ponds occurred in 1900, when 788,000 were struck. The reason for this sudden flurry of activity was the need to convert the Republic's gold reserves into a form that could be easily transported and shipped abroad, as the Boer War began to go badly for the Boers. In 1900 Pretoria was occupied by British troops and the mint was closed down.

Perrin, who had been appointed Master of the Mint in 1899, petitioned the British authorities to have the mint reopened. The home government felt that a branch of the Royal Mint would be feasible, but rejected the existing mint as far too small and cramped and offering no room for possible expansion. The Transvaal government was faced with the expense of paying off the debt of the old mint and funding the establishment of the new one, without much prospect of recouping these losses as the output was to be restricted to gold. Inevitably the plan was rejected at the time. Ordinary British coinage circulated freely in the Union of South Africa after it was formed in 1910.

Ironically, the outbreak of the First World War, which was to curb British production of sovereigns, was indirectly responsible for the revival of the Pretoria mint. The British government gave its consent to minting of local gold coinage, but purely as a temporary expedient if circumstances should render such a step unavoidable. In October 1917 the Transvaal provincial council urged the opening of the mint, but under wartime emergency regulations the South African mines were obliged to sell their gold direct to the Bank of England. Much of this gold was shipped to India for refining and coining at the Royal Mint's branch in Bombay.

In the immediate post-war period, consideration was again given to opening a South African mint. Although the Chamber of Mines felt that it would be inadvisable to open a local mint in view of the small amount of gold coin required for local currency needs, the banks and the general public as a whole were strongly in favour. It seemed wasteful and expensive to ship gold abroad to be coined and re-imported. The South African government decided to press on with its proposals, and when it was calculated how much money had been lost by sending gold abroad, even the mining industry was won over. The South Africa Mint Act was drafted in 1919 and finally passed into law, paving the way for the establishment of a branch of the Royal Mint at Pretoria. This originally envisaged only the striking of gold, as in Australia and Canada, but a further Coinage Act (1922) prescribed the specifications for silver and bronze coins. Finally the Pretoria Mint Proclamation of 14th December 1922 authorised the

The last branch to be opened was at Pretoria, which began minting operations in 1923.

The Canadian George V sovereign of 1913 is rarity 4 on the Marsh rarity scale (see price guide).

Coinage Act of 1870 and with effect from 1st January 1923.

The Convent Redoubt on Visagie Street, originally a nunnery and later a prison, was the site of the new mint. The Deputy Master in charge was R.G.J. Pearson, previously Chief Assayer at the Ottawa Mint, while C.R. Robson, formerly of the Bombay branch mint, was appointed Assayer. Other managerial appointments, as well as those of all the foremen, were filled from the Royal Mint and its overseas branches. The Royal Mint, Pretoria, as it was officially styled, was formally opened on 2nd October 1923 by HRH the Duke of Connaught and the first two sovereigns were struck by his wife, Princess Alexandra.

Actual minting operations began earlier in the year, the first silver pieces being struck in May 1923, followed by small quantities of gold and bronze. The gold coins consisted of sovereigns and half-sovereigns identical to the British coins in every respect, save for the inclusion of the mintmark SA above the date. Fewer than 600 ordinary sovereigns were struck in 1923, making this the smallest mintage of any in the entire sovereign series, although proofs were also struck for inclusion in the sets prepared in the inaugural year. Like the first Ottawa sovereigns, the inaugural issue from South Africa is of the highest rarity nowadays. Output was not much greater the following year, when around two and a half thousand sovereigns were struck, and they also rank among the great rarities.

Production rose dramatically in 1925, when over six million were struck. South African sovereigns were minted annually in ever-increasing numbers, peaking in 1928, when 18,235,057 were produced. Thereafter output gradually declined up to 1931, when 8,511,792 were minted. The sovereigns of 1925-31 are all very common. The cataclysmic events of 1931, which led to Britain leaving the Gold Standard, resulted in the production of sovereigns at Pretoria ceasing in 1932 after some 1,066,680 had been minted that year. These coins are now rated as normal. Since that time Pretoria's gold has been confined to South African coins.

The Branch Mints Today

The Sydney branch mint was closed in 1926, while both Melbourne and Perth ceased producing sovereigns in 1931. Melbourne stopped operations at the end of June 1968 while Perth ceased to be a branch by proclamation of 29 May 1970. In 1931, responsibility for the Ottawa branch mint passed from the UK government to the Canadian federal government and the establishment was then renamed the Royal Canadian Mint. Branch mint status was withdrawn from Pretoria in 1941, when control passed to the South African government. The sovereign production of the branch mints belonged to a bygone era, when gold was the principal medium of exchange. It is interesting, however, to note that the former branch mints have played a decisive part in the dawning of the modern gold era: the Krugerrand struck at Pretoria since 1967, the Maple Leaf from Ottawa and, more recently, the Koala from Australia. Even the old Perth Mint has been revived for the production of the Nugget bullion series and is now a very active mint. For once, the former branch mints led the way, and in emulation of their success the Royal Mint has inaugurated its own bullion coin, in the shape of the Britannia.

In the annals of the sovereign, branch mints played an outstanding part, creating many of the rarities and helping to stimulate the world-wide interest and demand of collectors today.

THE ROLE OF THE SOVEREIGN

When the sovereign was revived in 1817, it was intended primarily as a unit of currency. The world price of gold was sufficiently stable at the time for the British government to take the courageous step of introducing a coin whose intrinsic value was very close to its face value. Hitherto, silver had fulfilled this function, but as the value of the white metal had fluctuated, it often had disastrous consequences for the money in general circulation. The change in emphasis from silver to gold was signalled by Britain abandoning the principles of bimetallism (a currency based on two metals, gold and silver, in a fixed ratio to each other) and embracing instead the concept of monometallism, in which one metal - gold - was the currency absolute and everything else, including silver, had merely token value.

The Gold Standard

The Gold Standard, which Britain effectively adopted in 1816 but which was not formally recognised as such until 1821, may be defined as the monetary system in which the unit of currency is, or is kept at the value of, a fixed weight of gold. This system evolved quite simply after 1816 from the free circulation of coinage, the free melting and free movement of gold. Under this system, anyone had the right to tender gold in unlimited quantities to the monetary authorities and to receive in exchange an equal weight of gold in the coin of the realm. There was also the implicit freedom to melt down coins, of which the weight and fineness was specified and unchanging, for their gold content. Gold coin and gold bullion could, at that time, be imported and exported without let or hindrance. All of these processes were carried on with little or no seigniorage or any other governmentally imposed charges.

When convertible paper currency gradually rivalled and eventually supplanted the use of sovereigns in everyday transactions, the same result was attained through an offer by the monetary authorities to buy or sell gold in unlimited quantities at a fixed price in convertible paper money per unit of weight of the metal, and to continue to refrain from placing any restriction on the free movement or trade in gold coin or gold bullion.

Eventually, there were three different gold standards in operation. The full Gold Standard, which operated until the outbreak of the First World War in August 1914, saw gold sovereigns in general circulation, giving 20 shillings' worth of goods and services. The Bank of England issued paper money in denominations from £5 upwards, which it was obliged to redeem on demand in gold at a fixed rate. The Bank was also compelled to buy and sell gold in unlimited quantities at a fixed price.

The Gold Bullion Standard was in operation from 1925 until 1931. In this period sovereigns did not circulate, and the Bank of England was only bound to buy and sell gold in bars of 400 ounces, the current price then being £1,700. The result of this was that the Bank of England only bought and sold gold in large quantities. This fulfilled the needs of bankers, who had foreign exchange differences to settle, but prevented gold from dribbling into internal circulation.

The Gold Exchange Standard enjoyed considerable vogue up to 1931. By this system the Bank of England was not bound to buy and sell gold, but only to buy and sell bills, cheques and other instruments drawn in currencies on the full gold or gold bullion standards.

Britain was the first - and for many years the only - country to adopt the Gold Standard. This is all the more surprising as Russia was the world's leading producer of gold in the mid-nineteenth century, closely followed, from 1849

A leather sovereign case.

consumed some 6,489 tons of gold, although much of this was recoined sovereigns. By comparison, the United States coined only 3,477 tons of gold between 1793 and 1913, while Russia, the world's largest actual producer of the raw material in this period, struck 1,287 tons of gold between 1800 and 1914. This was actually exceeded by the German Empire, whose output of gold coin between 1872 and 1914 was more than 1,900 tons. The output of gold coins of the world's five principal trading nations in the nineteenth century amounted to no less than 13,565 tons, comfortably exceeding the total production of 'new' gold in the same period (about 12,300 tons).

The End of the Gold Standard

onwards, by the United States. To be sure, Britain profited largely from the spectacular discoveries of gold in Australia (1851), South Africa (1884) and the Yukon (1896), but Britain's reliance on the yellow metal, as demonstrated by the output of sovereigns, was largely dictated by the meteoric expansion of its international commerce. Portugal adopted the Gold Standard in 1854, followed by Switzerland (1860), the German Empire (1872), the Scandinavian countries, Belgium and France (1873), the Netherlands and Italy (1875), Finland (1877), Romania (1890), Austria-Hungary (1892), India (1893), Chile (1895), Russia and Japan (1897) and the United States (1900). The adoption in 1893 of an imperfect version of the Gold Exchange Standard by India - hitherto a staunch advocate of the silver standard - ushered in an era in which an international Gold Standard may be said to be in full operation. After 1900 only China, Mexico and a few small countries remained as representatives of the silver standard. By 1914 the Gold Standard operated throughout the civilised world, although in many cases gold circulated in a fixed ratio to silver. Ironically, in 1931 - the year that many countries, including Britain, were forced off the Gold Standard - Switzerland actually embraced a pure Gold Standard and abandoned bimetallism.

The sovereigns and half-sovereigns, and the £2 and £5 pieces which occasionally supplemented the series, contained full value; that is to say, their face value was exactly the same as their intrinsic value as defined by their statutory parity. Between 1817 and 1914 the sovereigns and other gold coins struck at the Royal Mint and its branches in Australia

The supremacy of the Gold Standard was short-lived and covered only the two decades from 1894 till the outbreak of the First World War. That war saw recourse to inconvertible paper money in nearly every country. Monetary units were then no longer based on a commodity asset - gold - but were only the uncallable debts of the issuing authorities. Paper money became legally acceptable at its face value and the traditional check on note issue (which had hitherto been limited by the amount of gold held in a bank's or the nation's reserves) was abandoned. This freed governments from the constraints of gold, and gave them the liberty to regulate their money supply according to economic or political needs.

Gold ceased to be used in internal payment systems, but in international banking gold tended to play as big a role as ever. After the First World War, and throughout the Twenties, there was a general tendency to revert to the Gold Standard, and by 1928 it had largely recovered its pre-war position. It had no sooner been re-established, however, when it was hit hard by bank collapse in Austria, the Wall Street crash of 1929 and the widespread economic depression. Britain temporarily suspended the Gold Standard in 1931, but what began as a purely temporary measure soon became permanent. By 1937 there was not a single country that could be said to be fairly and squarely on the Gold Standard. By that time the tremendous advantages of inconvertible paper currencies were recognised.

After August 1914 gold coins lost their primary function as a medium of exchange in everyday circulation, and became purely and simply articles of commerce, to be bought and sold at prices which were determined by the prevailing value of their gold content, together with a small premium based on supply and demand. An additional, and increasingly complicating, factor was government restriction on the free movement of gold. The sovereign was one of those coins which, in the inter-war period, was traded freely at little or no premium over its intrinsic value. This, in turn, often made banks reluctant to handle sovereigns and encouraged their melting down into bullion. It is impossible to estimate the quantity consigned to the melting pot in this period, but it must have been vast. The fate of the London sovereigns dated 1916 and 1917 has already been mentioned, but many other dates, once represented by substantial mintages, are now decidedly scarce, particularly in the more collectable grades of condition.

In the period immediately after the Second World War, a general lack of confidence in the economy created a demand for sovereigns, which were the ideal medium for the small saver and investor seeking a hedge against inflation and also the innate sense of security which gold had provided since time immemorial. The rising demand for sovereigns for this purpose inevitably forced up the market value which, in turn, fuelled further public demand. This rise in the market for 'bullion' gold coins did not affect the normal bullion market (in bars and ingots), as the latter maintained equilibrium through the output of the gold mines, which kept pace with world demand.

This was a period in which there was a finite quantity of actual gold coins, and even this was diminishing year by year as existing gold coins continued to be melted down, or converted into jewellery and related products. Official policy world-wide did not countenance the minting of new gold coins to any extent. It is significant, for example, that although gold coins were struck by the Royal Mint in 1953, the year of the Queen's Coronation, none was ever made available to the public. The premium on sovereigns gave rise to extensive counterfeiting, especially in Italy and Syria. There was a small well-organised distribution network supplying Switzerland, France, Germany and Greece.

The British Government launched a successful two-pronged attack on the counterfeiters. They sought protection for the sovereign in European courts, while also resuming production to squeeze the premium and make counterfeiting less profitable.

Interestingly, as the demand for sovereigns from investors waned due to increases in the premium, the demand from the numismatic market began to rise. There was a time, in the 1950s and early 1960s, when sovereigns were still traded freely, regardless of their date, design or mintmark. By the time that it had dawned on the buying public (whether investors or collectors) that there were differences in the coins which could considerably affect their value, the majority of the rare and scarce items had probably already disappeared into the hands of collectors. Nevertheless, there have been some remarkable instances in more recent years when substantial quantities of sovereigns have been released on to the market and have yielded some of the major rarities.

Sunken Treasure

In 1932 an Italian salvage team commenced the recovery of some 90,000 sovereigns from the wreck of P&O Steamer Egypt, which had sunk a decade earlier in a collision near the Ile d'Ouessant (Ushant) off the Brittany coast. Most of the coins were immediately returned to the bullion market but, in the style of those gentlemanly days, a small number of coins were retained as souvenirs of their unexpected recovery. They were placed in leather boxes with the gilt arms of Lloyd's - the most famous name in maritime insurance - emblazoned on the lid and with a printed certificate.

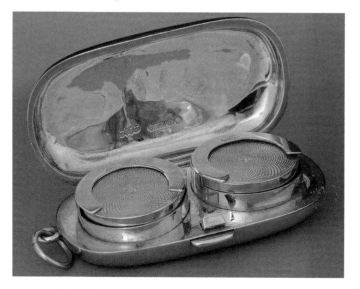

Spring-loaded cases were used for gold coins required for everyday transactions. With rings for suspension on watch chains, they could be conveniently carried in the fob of a waistcoat.

More recently, there was the recovery of the bullion cargo from the holds of the Royal Mail Steamer Douro. Its subsequent sale at auction in November 1996 was surely the largest hoard of gold sovereigns to be successfully sold. The fear that the market would be swamped by the sheer volume of coins available proved without foundation.

The value of the cargo on board the RMS Douro when it sank after a collision in 1882 was in excess of £50,000. The auction sale - which was a long way short of the full cargo - realised a little over £1,500,000, making the average price for a single sovereign around £175. However, the breakdown of the cargo is not that simple. The bullion - for there was no added numismatic value in 1882 - was mostly in the form of gold sovereigns being transferred from Australia to London. Some coins were from as early as the reign of George IV, and could have made their outward journey over fifty years prior to the catastrophe. The output of sovereigns year after year had been continuous and for some unaccountable reason - although there was obviously much duplication - the Douro was able to offer collectors London sovereigns with most dates from 1838 onwards.

When the RMS Douro sank, it was just five years after Queen Victoria had proclaimed herself Empress of India, and Britain was at the height of her Imperial powers. Whilst vast shipments of gold were not commonplace, the wheels that financed the Empire, and much beyond, were oiled with gold - mainly British gold sovereigns. The majority of London-minted sovereigns recovered from the Douro were of an amazing quality, which implied that they had been secured in bank strong rooms and were not simply coins removed from circulation. They had presumably arrived in Australia as a bullion payment, remained untouched for a number of years, and were being returned as part of another bullion payment. As for the Australian sovereigns, it is a misconception that they were made for local use - with the size of the country and the smallness of its population, there really was very little need for them locally. The coins were almost exclusively made for shipment overseas and again those recovered were 'as new'.

The Douro coins were very attractive to collectors. They were new to the market and had the romance of a sea-salvage history; they covered a wide range of dates and were mostly in excellent condition - gold does not deteriorate under water, although some coins picked up a red patina from the rusting hull. There were even some unpublished varieties, unknown even to the Royal Mint. Known rarities included the narrow shield 1843, the Ansell 1859, and the 1863 sovereign with the figures 827 on the truncation of the neck. The highest price at the auction, which was paid independently for two separate coins, was £4,840, whilst a number of coins reached prices which were nearly as high - a demonstration of the strength of the numismatic market in the United Kingdom. A separate, flourishing market in Australia, and an especial shortage of Australian-minted sovereigns within that market, had buyers bidding these coins to unexpectedly high levels. Coins with this prestigious pedigree will continue to be seen on the market for many years.

International Currency

In recent years the Ministry of Defence has disposed of its stock of sovereigns through the medium of tenders from registered bullion dealers, and inevitably these have included a number of elusive items. Aficionados of James Bond will recall how, in 'From Russia with Love', British agents were supplied with belts containing sovereigns. Whether this incident bore any relation to reality is conjectural, but it is incontrovertible that the Ministry of Defence has, over a long period, acquired vast sums in sovereigns for the purpose of paying agents and funding operations. The Arabs who supported Colonel Lawrence in his activities during the First World War, for example, were paid in sovereigns. From time to time there are rumours of banks which are alleged to have vast stocks of sovereigns in their vaults, and apocryphal tales of numismatists fortunate enough to get the opportunity to check over these stocks in order to extract the rarities lying undetected and unconsidered.

Counterfeiter or Businessman?

After Britain came off the Gold Standard in 1931 it became illegal to use sovereigns in Great Britain. This led to an unusual court case involving Jose Beraha Zdravko. Born in Skopje, Yugoslavia on 14th December 1907, Beraha trained in a local business college where he showed an aptitude for commerce. He later became director of a leading local firm that specialised in foreign trade and also ran factories for treating oil and rice. In 1943 the Nazis occupied Yugoslavia and Beraha and two nephews escaped to Italy, where he set up a trading business exporting Milanese milling machines, aluminium ware and textiles to South America. Currencies fluctuated wildly from day to day and gold was in heavy demand; Italy and everywhere else wanted gold - especially the trusted British gold sovereign. Beraha studied the history of the sovereign and found that it was last officially issued for circulation in 1917 when it was worth one pound - then $4.86. A sovereign was near a quarter of an ounce of pure gold, so at the official world market price of $35 an ounce it was worth $8.75. Unofficially, it was selling for between $14 and $28 in local currencies.

Beraha reasoned that, following Britain's withdrawal from the Gold Standard, the sovereign was no longer legal tender in Great Britain. He consulted lawyers in England, Switzerland and Italy; they all agreed with Beraha - the British gold sovereign had become an international trade coin. In 1946 Beraha set up a factory in Via Andrea Doria and paid an engraver in Milan one hundred dollars for a pair of sovereign dies. Beraha wanted to produce a sovereign that was better than the Royal Mint product, so he put in more gold. Instead of getting 136.5 sovereigns out of every kilogram like the Royal Mint, Beraha produced 135 per kilo. They were all dated 1926, a year that the Royal Mint did not strike. He was able to make a profit of $700 on every kilo, with the coins mainly sold in China, India, North Africa and Arabia.

In 1951 Beraha decided to retire to Lugano, Switzerland after making two million dollars. In November of that year the British Government tracked down the source of the gold sovereigns and brought pressure on the Italian police to raid Via Andrea Doria and extradite Beraha from Switzerland, although as far as Beraha was concerned he had committed no crime. Due to the Swiss penal code he could not be bailed since he was being held for investigation, so he was in jail for seven months. Knowing that his case would depend on convincing the Swiss courts that the gold sovereign was no longer legal tender, he asked his Italian lawyer to travel to London with ten gold sovereigns to spend; he was unable to buy anything with them. In the summer of 1952 a unanimous decision was handed down by the five judges that Beraha should be released and on 18th November 1953 the Milan Court of Appeal ruled that the case against him be dismissed.

RMS Douro, which sank after a collision in 1882 with in excess of 50,000 sovereigns on board.

The Modern Gold Market

One result of the abrogation of the Gold Standard in 1931 was a depreciation of world currencies in terms of gold. Putting it another way, the price of gold rose. Some countries, including Britain, seized the opportunity to write up the value of their gold reserves, while the rise in the price of gold suddenly made gold-mining more profitable. Mines which had been abandoned on grounds of operating costs were re-opened and the world output of gold rose. World gold production in 1929 was 19.6 million ounces; it rose to 22.4 million ounces in 1932 and 35 million ounces in 1936. The Bank of England's gold reserves rose dramatically, from 146 millions in 1929 to 326 millions in 1937. In the same period, the US monetary gold stocks rose from $2,857 millions to $12,804 millions.

While the Gold Bullion Standard was in operation it was necessary to continue the production of gold sovereigns, hence the substantial output at the branch mints and the resumption of sovereigns from the Royal Mint itself. By 1925 Britain and other countries were operating the Gold Exchange Standard. The gold thus used came into and went out of Exchange Accounts, leaving the central gold reserves intact. Each country ran its own internal credit policy without having the supply of credit continually upset by changes in the size of its central bank's gold reserves. This was a decided advantage in the Thirties, when most of the exchange fluctuations and consequent gold movements were due to sudden transfers of capital about the world, and bore no relation to the internal and commercial financial position of a country.

This system worked surprisingly well and withstood the pressures of the Second World War. It formed the basis for the world monetary system devised at Bretton Woods in July 1944. The fixed exchange relationships between the world's currencies have gold as their common denominator, because the International Monetary Fund requires member countries to define their currency parities in terms of gold or the US dollar. As gold had a fixed parity of $35 an ounce (which the American government was pledged to honour), it continued to serve as the world's currency yardstick.

In the Fifties the United States controlled the vast bulk of the world's monetary gold reserves and this explains the popularity of the dollar as an international currency in this period. But as the world gradually recovered from the effects of the war, US balance of payments slid into deficit. When America's foreign liabilities began to exceed its dwindling gold reserves, the position became alarming. In the late Sixties there was a flight from the dollar into gold and this forced the Federal government to revoke its promise to redeem dollars in gold. On 15th August 1971 the dollar ceased to be convertible. Five months later, the dollar was devalued for the first time and the official price of gold rose from $35 to $38. This, in fact, lagged behind the free market price, which already stood at $40 an ounce. When the dollar was devalued for a second time early in 1973, the official gold price moved to $42.22 an ounce, but the free market price then stood at $70 an ounce.

The United States now favoured an international monetary system free from links to gold, but this was opposed by France and other countries in which there was a strong gold tradition. Eventually, the American viewpoint prevailed, and at the meeting of the IMF's Interim Committee in Jamaica in 1976, floating exchange rates were legalised and

the official gold price was abolished. Thereafter the price of gold on the world markets was allowed to rise and fall freely. In May 1973 the price of gold broke through the $100 barrier for the first time. By the end of 1974 it had doubled, but then dropped sharply. The slump was only temporary, however, and by the middle of 1978 the price had recovered. The sale of gold by the Carter administration to prop up the dollar depressed the price to $190, but increases in world oil prices pushed up the value of gold again.

Political uncertainty then took a hand. The American hostage crisis in Iran, the rise of Muslim fundamentalism in Arabia and, above all, the Soviet invasion of Afghanistan, combined to stimulate global demand for gold. In January 1980 gold rose successively to $600, then $700, and finally peaked on 21st January at $860 an ounce. These dramatic increases in the gold price triggered off a wave of speculation, exacerbated by the activities of the Hunt Brothers in Texas, among others, in attempting to corner the silver market. The bubble burst, and the price of gold subsided by March 1980 to $500. The outbreak of the Gulf War between Iran and Iraq and fears for the supply of oil drove the price of gold back to $720 in the autumn of 1980, but it subsequently dropped just as sharply, and throughout the 1980s drifted around the $400 level. In the wake of the October 1987 Stock Market crash it rose fleetingly to $500. At the end of the twentieth century its price fluctuated at around $300 per ounce.

This page and facing: 1989 Sovereign, 500th Anniversary of the first gold sovereign 1489-1989.

Revival of Gold Coinage

In Britain, the resumption of sovereign production in 1957 was dictated by the rising demand for these coins by small investors and to prevent counterfeiting. By that time the supply of older sovereigns was rapidly drying up, and the attentions of collectors were an added factor. The Royal Mint, it will be remembered, had restruck sovereigns dated 1925 in 1949-52, but in general it eschewed the practice of continuing to issue coins with a frozen date, although this was adopted in other countries (e.g. the Austrian ducats dated 1915 and the Russian chervonetz dated 1923). Production of sovereigns since 1957, though aimed primarily at the bullion market, at least had the saving grace of changing the date to accord with

the actual year of minting - a policy that not only gave confidence to the bullion market but encouraged numismatic interest. Thus, at a time when countries were either re-striking old coins or, like South Africa, turning attention to one-ounce bullion pieces, the Royal Mint provided a shining example by injecting new life and interest into an old and well-tried favourite. Pistrucci's St George and Dragon remained immutable, but the bust of the young Queen on the obverse, later replaced by a more mature portrait (1974), undoubtedly helped to popularise the modern sovereign with the collector and the lay public.

Output of sovereigns rose in the early Sixties, a period when numismatics enjoyed a popularity unparalleled in its history. Unfortunately, just as the boom was escalating, the government intervened to place serious restrictions on the possession of gold coins in general, and the sovereign in particular.

Prior to 1931, a sovereign was worth 20 shillings and was legal tender for that amount. Since 1931 its market value has risen out of all recognition, but it remains to this day legal tender for one pound sterling. In the immediate post-war years, however, the government was impelled to place some restriction on the movement of gold in order to prevent hoarding by private individuals or a drain abroad of the country's precious reserves. In 1947, for example, the sovereign at home was worth about 50 shillings, but on the French black market it traded at 100 shillings, and the following year actually rose as high as 128 shillings.

The Exchange Control Act

Obviously it would have been an extremely lucrative proposition for speculators in Britain to export sovereigns to France and profit by the high prices obtained there. The British Government, however, made such a proposition illegal by introducing the Exchange Control Act in 1947, which laid down that 'no person other than an authorised dealer should buy, borrow, lend or sell any gold or foreign currency'. Moreover, it stipulated that 'any person possessing gold should offer it for sale to an authorised dealer at a price not exceeding the authorised price, unless the Treasury consented to his retention of the gold'. This Act would have posed serious problems for the numismatist, had not the Exchange Control (Collectors' Pieces Exemption) Order 1947 been brought into force simultaneously. This allowed collectors to hold on to 'any gold coin which was minted in 1816 or earlier, and any gold coin which was minted after 1816 and which has a numismatic value greater than the value of the gold content which would have been received if the coin had been sold to an authorised [bullion] dealer'. In effect, this meant that numismatists and coin dealers were not hindered from buying and selling gold coins as long as the coins were in collectable condition and possessed numismatic interest.

No check was made on numismatists to see that they kept to the regulations, however, and it has to be conceded that a great amount of trading was carried out in the early Sixties in sovereigns per se and not as collectors' pieces. By the mid-1960s, interest in gold as a hedge against inflation had risen to unprecedented heights and advertisements appeared quite openly (in the Personal columns of the 'quality' Sunday newspapers, for example) offering sovereigns for £3 10s each, or as little as £320 per hundred.

This blatant disregard of the terms of the 1947 Act and its attendant Exemption Order coincided with a remarkable phenomenon which can only be described as the gold medal craze. This fashion was, in fact, triggered off in 1963, when the Polynesian kingdom of Tonga issued a set of three gold coins, in denominations of one, half and quarter koula (koula being the Tongan word for gold). At the time, great stress was laid on the fact that these were the first gold coins placed into circulation at their face value as part of a nation's currency since the world-wide abandonment of the Gold Standard more than thirty years previously. The koula (with a face value of £16 sterling) was naively described as the highest denomination of any gold coin placed in actual circulation for almost two centuries, but when it is realised that £16 represented slightly more than the average annual income in Tonga, it will be seen that very few of these large and handsome pieces could ever have passed from hand to hand in the course of normal business transactions in Polynesia!

Another novel feature at the time was the strict limit of mintage (1,500 koula, 3,000 half-koula and 6,300 quarter-koula, together with a minute quantity of proofs). Sets could be obtained from the Crown Agents in London at £28 10s, but the global publicity for the issue captured the imagination of collectors and investors everywhere and in no time at all the set was trading at £150.

The runaway success of the Tongan gold coins of 1963 is indicative of the thirst for modern gold pieces which was to spread the following year when the 400th anniversary of the birth of Shakespeare was marked by various issues of gold medals aimed at the collector market. A rash of similar issues followed in quick succession. In 1965 the output of commemorative gold medals doubled again, and significantly there were several coin issues as well. The Isle of Man issued sovereigns, half-sovereigns and £5 pieces to celebrate the 200th anniversary of the Revestment Act, but the island's parliament, the Tynwald, omitted to have the coins declared legal tender. This did not affect the inordinate demand for the coins at the time of issue.

The Exchange Control Order

The issue of sets of gold medals proliferated and culminated with the launch of an ambitious series planned in 1966 to portray the Prime Ministers of Britain since Walpole. Suddenly, the Labour government pricked the gold bubble by introducing the Exchange Control (Gold Coins Exemption) Order 1966. The object of the Order, which came into effect on 27th April that year, was to prevent the loss of currency reserves caused by the import of gold coins and medals from abroad and to eliminate the hoarding of gold by speculators - as opposed to genuine coin collectors, who nevertheless were now to be subject to strict control.

By the terms of this Order, no-one was permitted to hold more than four gold coins minted after 1837, unless they had received express permission from the Treasury. The maximum was set at four coins so that people who had one or two sovereigns as mementoes could keep them without breaking the law. The Order gave rise to a paradoxical - not to say nonsensical - situation: the Treasury maintained on the one hand that sovereigns were still legal tender, but on the other hand now made it illegal for the average British citizen to possess them.

Permission to possess more than four post-1837 gold coins was only granted by the Treasury after the would-be collector had completed a very detailed form. This required fairly precise details of the existing collection. Each post-1837 gold coin held at the time had to be listed, along with a detailed description. The purpose of this inquisition was obvious, but the form then went on to demand the number and approximate value of the pre-1838 gold coins in the collection. Furthermore, holdings of silver coins minted after 1919, between 1816 and 1919, and before 1816, as well as base metal coins before and after 1860, had to be disclosed. The object was apparently to prove to the satisfaction of the Treasury the genuineness of a collector's numismatic interests, but the petty bureaucracy and official prying into the affairs of the private individual was regarded as sinister and many gave up collecting sovereigns at this time rather than submit to such an inquisition.

Those who obtained the necessary permission from the Bank of England to collect post-1837 gold coins could do so only on the condition that they kept no more than two examples of any given coin (different dates, mintmarks and die variations being regarded as distinct types). Any duplicates above that number had to be sold to an authorised dealer. It cannot be denied that the effect of such forced sales gravely affected the market.

In the rigorous attempt to control gold collecting, the Treasury made no distinction between ordinary specie used as a medium of exchange on the international market and items of pure numismatic interest, such as proofs and patterns, which could not be regarded as part of the nation's gold reserves. Yet post-1837 coins which had been mounted for use as cufflinks, brooches or bracelets were deemed to be jewellery and, as such, were exempt from the 1966 Order. The possession of gold medals was not outwardly affected, but the purchase of such items was now forbidden and the manufacture of them virtually came to a standstill.

A few unlucky collectors were caught breaking the law and prosecuted, their collections being confiscated. Undoubtedly, many more flouted the law and continued to hold on to their hoard of sovereigns without being able to buy or sell further. The main effect of this piece of legislation was to undermine the position of London as the centre of the world coin market. Gold trading fled abroad and flourished as

The millennium sovereign,
which is the first currency issue since 1982.

never before in European countries free from such restrictions, to the detriment of the traditional British market. The manufacturers of commemorative medals quickly discovered a loophole in the law, and turned their attention instead to palladium, platinum and other precious metals which had not hitherto received much consideration. Significantly, Tonga capped its previous success with a series of coins in 1967, which included three struck in palladium.

Sanity returned to the sovereign market in 1973, when the Conservative government rescinded the 1966 Order. For a short time collectors were allowed to buy and sell gold coins at will. In 1974, however, following the return of the Labour

Above: The Tower Hill Mint, with part of the Tower, c1810.
Below: An aerial photograph showing the present Royal Mint at Llantrisant in Wales.

government, a modified version of the Order was re-imposed. This, too, was abolished after the Conservatives were returned to power in 1979. In more recent years, the British market in sovereigns, as in other gold coins, has been hampered to some extent by the imposition of Value Added Tax. Nevertheless, the British coin trade has managed to survive these vicissitudes and compete with its European and American rivals.

If government controls and taxes may be regarded as having had a dampening effect on the sovereign market from time to time, it should be pointed out that credit for the upsurge of interest in the sovereign in recent years is due to the Royal Mint. In 1979 the Royal Mint recognised the potent force of the modern numismatic market and began producing proof versions of the sovereign. This marked a major breakthrough, for previously the Mint had aimed its products primarily at the bullion market. This coincided with the adoption of a more imaginative and aggressive marketing policy on a global scale which, more than anything else, was to make the numismatic world fully conscious of the attraction and potential of the sovereign series. Of course, the Royal Mint is in the business of selling modern coins, but there can be no doubt that the publicity given to recent issues - most notably the 1989 series marking the Quincentenary of the Sovereign - has injected new life into the market for the sovereign series as a whole.

Despite the vicissitudes of the the twentieth century the sovereign has established itself as a prized item of coin collectors the world over.

THE
SOVEREIGN PRICE GUIDE

George III

George IV

Victoria

William IV

Edward VII

Elizabeth II

George V

ADVICE TO COLLECTORS

A book such as this may well stimulate an interest in collecting gold sovereigns. Collecting antiques has been made popular by numerous television programmes and easy access to books of reference, but the one common theme to all forms of collecting, from paintings to teddy bears, fountain pens to classical antiquities, and all in between, is the constant emphasis on quality. So with gold sovereigns it is the quality of the individual coins that determines the strength and value of a collection. The new collector is advised to buy the best that can be afforded, but for the rarer and scarcer prices one might have to compromise condition in order to complete the date sequences. With a growing collection 'bad buys' and lesser grade coins can always be sold off when a better replacement is found. Many dealers publish lists and, to a certain extent, the collection can be built up by mail order. Likewise, at all auctions, a bid can be placed by mail - one does not to have to sit through endless sales, fearful of twitching at the wrong moment, and becoming the immediate owner of some unwanted piece!

There are always ample opportunities for those who wish to build up a collection. Many dealers attend small trade shows, where their stock is displayed for sale. Coin shows or fairs do not have the outward glamour of the splendid London antique fairs, but they are well attended and fun. For well over a decade, the British Numismatic Trade Association has been running an international show, called COINEX, which is held each October in London. Attending such shows gives the collector the chance to meet more than one dealer at a time, and all dealers, ever hopeful of a sale, like to talk about every aspect of collecting.

PRICE GUIDE

A 'Price Guide' is just that, no more, no less. For many years, it has been common practice to list collectable items in catalogues, and coins are no exception. Several nineteenth-century dealers in the United Kingdom and in Europe provided their clients with lists of items for sale. It was a time when prices seldom changed and supply was bountiful. As a result the catalogues were kept as a source of reference. The first Standard Catalogue of British Coins was published by the then active London dealers, B.A. Seaby, in 1929, and whilst the dealing side of that company has ceased trading, the catalogue is still published. It is one of the editors of that publication, Brian Reeds, who specialized in British coins, who has provided the price structure that follows.

Investors will know that the bullion price of gold is 'fixed' each day in a quaint ceremony of raising and lowering of flags. This price very much controls the trading price for a gold sovereign when the coin is one from a year of large mintage figures, and when the coin is in unexceptional condition, and not one that would be desired by specialist collectors of rarity. The bullion price is not free from manipulation, but in recent years the variance in price has been slight.

A collector of some substance might be tempted to amass huge quantities of sovereigns, in the hopes of finding some that are rarer than others. Such a collector might just be lucky, once in a blue moon! Collectors of lesser means are advised to look elsewhere. It is obvious that dealers cannot afford to stockpile vast quantities of sovereigns as it would soon become too expensive. But the coins that dealers do hold tend to be of the higher grades of condition, along with the scarce and rare dates.

Major auction houses list the scarce and rare coins in the catalogues for their general coin and medal sales. There are advantages in studying sale catalogues, and much fresh material comes onto the market through sales at auction houses. Coins are listed in a logical sequence, and sovereigns will be found in date order. At most auction houses help and advice on buying - and selling - sovereigns, or indeed any coins or medals, is freely given.

A collector has to remember that all Price Guides have to be very much a matter of opinion. The better the grade of the coin, the more it is worth, but the actual grading is also a little subjective. Collectors should be wary of buying coins that are listed in a high grade, yet priced cheaply - for it is almost inevitable that the coin will be overgraded. The rarity scale has been based on the quantities of coins that might become available in the market-place, and a rare date coin is still a rare date, even if, for instance, the coin has been pierced for jewellery. Experience will soon teach the collector just how hard it is to buy certain sovereigns in choice condition.

GRADING AND RARITY

The traditional terminology of grading has been used in this book. The rarity value reflects the system pioneered by Michael Marsh in his book, *The Gold Sovereign*, Common, Normal and Scarce, and the degrees of rarity run from R, Rare, to R7, the highest rarity possible. Grading is the term that covers the state of preservation or condition of the coin. The disparity in the price between a worn coin and a specimen in mint state, or UNC, allows a further graduated condition rating, such as 'nearly' and 'good' before each basic grade, for example; nearly EF and good EF. The lowest grade mentioned in the Price Guide is Nearly Fine (NF), improving by degrees to Mint State (MS), or Uncirculated (UNC).

Poor A very worn coin, of no value as a collector's piece unless extremely rare.

Fair A coin that is worn, but which has the inscriptions and main features of the design still distinguishable, or a piece that is very weakly struck.

Fine A coin with considerable wear, that can be scratched or otherwise marked, and which may have striking imperfections.

Very Fine A coin that shows signs of having been in limited circulation, with wear to the high spots, such as the monarch's hair.

Extremely Fine A coin that shows no obvious signs of having been in circulation, but which might, when looked at closely, be seen to have some very minor imperfections.

Uncirculated/Mint State These terms mean just what they say. Modern coins (and the starting date of 1817 is, in this respect, modern) were issued from the Mint in bags of a certain total value. Coins from these bags would not have been in general circulation, but by the very nature of their manufacture or distribution they might not be truly 'perfect' specimens.

FDC Fleur-de-coin. Flawless, unused, without any wear, scratches or marks. Usually only applied to proofs.

Proof Coinage Throughout the period of the listing, and especially with recent issues, 'Proof' coins have been issued. 'Proof' is not a term of condition or preservation. A Proof coin has been struck from specially prepared and polished dies that give the field of the coin a mirror-like surface. The one exception is the Proof coinage of 1902, struck to commemorate the coronation of King Edward VII. All the coins in these presentation sets, the gold sovereign included, were struck with a matt, or 'dull frosted', surface. Serious collectors may well expand their horizons to include proofs alongside the regular or currency issues. In 1937 gold proof sets were issued containing five and two pound pieces sovereign and half sovereign and were not issued for general circulation. All four coins have Pistrucci's St George reverse.

Collectors from overseas may be familiar with the MS grading system used in the United States, where the ideal perfect coin could be MS 70, whilst MS 65 is about as good as one might be able to get. The wide range of the price column, from the lowest to the highest, gives a variety of prices, and those used to the US system will be able to follow the price/grade columns without problems.

Fine   *Very Fine*   *Extremely Fine*   *Uncirculated/Mint State*

GEORGE III
1760-1820

Marsh No.	Date	Rarity	Type	£ NF	£ F	£ GF	£ NVF	£ VF	£ GVF	£ NEF	£ EF	£ GEF	£ UNC
1	1817	NORMAL	LAUR. HEAD	120	135	150	165	200	250	325	450	550	700
2	1818	NORMAL	LAUR. HEAD	135	150	165	175	200	250	375	500	625	800
2A	1818	SCARCE	LAUR. HEAD	135	150	165	175	225	275	400	550	650	850
2B	1818	SCARCE	LAUR. HEAD	135	150	165	175	225	275	400	550	650	850
2C	1818	RARE	LAUR. HEAD	150	165	175	200	250	300	450	600	725	975
3	1819	RARITY 6	LAUR. HEAD	4500	7500	10,000	20,000	30,000	50,000				
4	1820	SCARCE	LAUR. HEAD	135	150	165	175	225	275	400	550	650	850
4A	1820	RARE	LAUR. HEAD	150	165	175	200	250	300	450	600	725	975
4B	1820	RARE	LAUR. HEAD	150	165	175	200	250	300	450	600	725	975
4C	1820	RARITY 2	LAUR. HEAD	150	165	175	200	250	300	450	600	725	975

Marsh No. 2A   Ascending colon after BRITANNIAR·.
Marsh No. 2B   Wiry curls, legend as normal.
Marsh No. 2C   Wiry curls, legend as 2A.
Marsh No. 3   The highest condition recorded is good VF (7 known specimens).

Marsh No. 4A   Short date figures.
Marsh No. 4B   Small 0 in date.
Marsh No. 4C   1 in date is with a Roman I.

George III sovereign of 1817, Marsh No.1.

Marsh No.	Date	Rarity	Type	£ NF	£ F	£ GF	£ NVF	£ VF	£ GVF	£ NEF	£ EF	£ GEF	£ UNC
5	1821	NORMAL	LAUR. HEAD	95	100	110	120	175	200	275	450	500	650
6	1822	NORMAL	LAUR. HEAD	95	100	110	120	175	200	275	450	500	650
7	1823	RARITY 3	LAUR. HEAD	120	150	200	275	450	550	800	1200	1650	2000
8	1824	SCARCE	LAUR. HEAD	95	100	110	135	200	250	325	500	575	700
9	1825	RARITY 3	LAUR. HEAD	120	150	175	250	350	500	750	1000	1450	1800
10	1825	SCARCE	BARE HEAD	90	95	100	120	200	250	325	450	550	675
11	1826	NORMAL	BARE HEAD	90	95	100	120	160	200	275	400	450	575
12	1827	SCARCE	BARE HEAD	90	95	105	135	200	250	325	450	550	675
13	1828	RARITY 4	BARE HEAD	550	700	850	1250	1750	2200	2750	4000	4500	5500
14	1829	SCARCE	BARE HEAD	90	95	110	135	200	250	325	450	550	675
15	1830	SCARCE	BARE HEAD	90	95	110	135	200	250	325	450	550	675

Actual Size

Top: George IV Laureate Head sovereign of 1821, Marsh No.5.
Bottom: George IV Bare Head sovereign of 1830, Marsh No.15.

WILLIAM IV
1830–1837

Marsh No.	Date	Rarity	Type	£ NF	£ F	£ GF	£ NVF	£ VF	£ GVF	£ NEF	£ EF	£ GEF	£ UNC
16	1831	RARITY 2	BARE HEAD	110	120	135	150	225	275	350	500	575	750
16A	1831	RARITY 5	BARE HEAD	120	150	175	225	275	350	450	600	750	900
17	1832	SCARCE	BARE HEAD	110	120	135	150	200	250	300	450	525	650
17A	1832	SCARCE	BARE HEAD	110	120	135	150	200	250	300	450	525	650
18	1833	SCARCE	BARE HEAD	110	120	135	150	200	250	300	450	525	650
19	1835	RARE	BARE HEAD	120	135	150	175	225	275	350	500	575	750
20	1836	SCARCE	BARE HEAD	110	120	135	150	200	250	300	425	500	650
20A	1836	RARITY 2	BARE HEAD	120	150	175	225	275	350	450	600	750	900
21	1837	SCARCE	BARE HEAD	120	135	150	175	225	275	350	500	575	750
21A	1837	RARITY 3	BARE HEAD	150	175	225	275	350	450	600	750	900	1200

M16A   First bust, WW incuse without stops.
M17A   First bust, WW incuse with stops.
M20A   Second bust, rev. additional letter N above ANNO.
M21A   Second bust, 3 of date over 8.

William IV sovereign of 1832, Marsh No.17.

Marsh No.	Date	Rarity	Type	£ NF	£ F	£ GF	£ NVF	£ VF	£ GVF	£ NEF	£ EF	£ GEF	£ UNC
22	1838	RARE	YOUNG HEAD SHIELD	110	120	140	150	175	200	300	450	550	750
22A	1838	RARITY 3	YOUNG HEAD SHIELD	500	600	800	1250	2000	2750	3500	4000	4500	5500
23	1839	RARITY 2	YOUNG HEAD SHIELD	110	135	150	250	275	375	650	900	1100	1450
24	1841	RARITY 3	YOUNG HEAD SHIELD	350	500	600	750	900	1250	2000	2750	3750	4750
25	1842	NORMAL	YOUNG HEAD SHIELD	75	80	85	90	100	120	150	175	225	300
26	1843	NORMAL	YOUNG HEAD SHIELD	75	80	85	90	100	120	150	175	225	300
26A	1843	RARITY 3	YOUNG HEAD SHIELD	500	600	800	1250	2000	2750	3500	4000	4500	5500
26B	1843/2	RARITY 5	YOUNG HEAD SHIELD	150	175	225	275	300	600	950	1500	2250	3000
27	1844	SCARCE	YOUNG HEAD SHIELD	80	85	90	95	110	135	175	225	275	350
27A	1844	RARITY 2	YOUNG HEAD SHIELD	110	135	150	250	275	375	475	600	750	900
28	1845	SCARCE	YOUNG HEAD SHIELD	80	85	90	95	110	135	175	225	275	350
29	1846	SCARCE	YOUNG HEAD SHIELD	80	85	90	95	110	135	175	225	275	350
30	1847	NORMAL	YOUNG HEAD SHIELD	75	80	85	90	100	120	150	175	225	300
31	1848	SCARCE	YOUNG HEAD SHIELD	80	85	90	95	110	135	175	225	275	350
31A	1848	RARITY 2	YOUNG HEAD SHIELD	110	135	150	250	275	375	475	600	750	900
32	1849	RARE	YOUNG HEAD SHIELD	85	90	95	100	120	150	200	250	300	400
33	1850	RARE	YOUNG HEAD SHIELD	85	90	95	100	120	150	200	250	300	400
34	1851	NORMAL	YOUNG HEAD SHIELD	75	80	85	90	100	120	150	175	225	300
35	1852	COMMON	YOUNG HEAD SHIELD	70	75	80	85	95	110	135	150	200	250
36	1853	COMMON	YOUNG HEAD SHIELD	70	75	80	85	95	110	135	150	200	250
37	1854	NORMAL	YOUNG HEAD SHIELD	75	80	85	90	100	120	150	175	225	300

M22A   More compact floral emblems within rev. shield.   M26B   3 of date over 2.   M31A   Small head.

M26A   Considerably modified floral emblems within rev. shield.   M27A   First 4 in date over inverted 4.

Victoria Young Head sovereign of 1852, Marsh No. 35.   *Actual Size*

Marsh No.	Date	Rarity	Type	£ NF	£ F	£ GF	£ NVF	£ VF	£ GVF	£ NEF	£ EF	£ GEF	£ UNC
38	1855	COMMON	YOUNG HEAD SHIELD	70	75	80	85	95	110	135	150	200	250
39	1856	NORMAL	YOUNG HEAD SHIELD	75	80	85	90	100	120	150	175	225	300
40	1857	NORMAL	YOUNG HEAD SHIELD	75	80	85	90	100	120	150	175	225	300
41	1858	RARE	YOUNG HEAD SHIELD	85	90	95	100	120	150	200	250	300	400
42	1859	RARE	YOUNG HEAD SHIELD	85	90	95	100	120	150	200	250	300	400
42A	1859	RARITY 4	YOUNG HEAD SHIELD	150	175	225	275	350	600	950	1500	2250	3000
43	1860	SCARCE	YOUNG HEAD SHIELD	80	85	90	95	110	135	175	225	275	350
44	1861	COMMON	YOUNG HEAD SHIELD	70	75	80	85	95	110	135	150	200	250
44A	1861	RARITY 2	YOUNG HEAD SHIELD	110	125	150	225	275	300	400	500	650	900
45	1862	COMMON	YOUNG HEAD SHIELD	70	75	80	85	95	110	135	150	200	250
45A	1862	RARITY 2	YOUNG HEAD SHIELD	110	125	150	225	275	300	400	500	650	900
46	1863	COMMON	YOUNG HEAD SHIELD	70	75	80	85	95	110	135	150	200	250
46A	1863	RARITY 6	YOUNG HEAD SHIELD	750	950	1500	2500	3500	4000	4500	5500	6000	7000
48	1863	NORMAL	YH SHIELD DIE NO.	75	80	85	90	100	120	150	175	225	300
48A	1863	RARITY 5	YH SHIELD DIE NO.	500	950	1250	2000	2750	3250	3750	4500	5000	6000
49	1864	COMMON	YH SHIELD DIE NO.	70	75	80	85	95	110	135	150	200	250
50	1865	SCARCE	YH SHIELD DIE NO.	80	85	90	95	110	135	175	225	275	350
51	1866	COMMON	YH SHIELD DIE NO.	70	75	80	85	95	110	135	150	200	250
52	1868	NORMAL	YH SHIELD DIE NO.	75	80	85	90	100	120	150	175	225	300
53	1869	COMMON	YH SHIELD DIE NO.	70	75	80	85	95	110	135	150	200	250
54	1870	NORMAL	YH SHIELD DIE NO.	75	80	85	90	100	120	150	175	225	300
55	1871	COMMON	YH SHIELD DIE NO.	70	75	80	85	95	110	135	150	200	250
84	1871	COMMON	YOUNG HEAD ST. GEORGE	70	75	80	85	95	105	110	130	150	200

M42A   Ansell sovereign, additional raised line on the lower part of the ribbon.

44A   1 in date with a Roman I.
45A   Inverted A under letter F in DEF.

46A   Figure 827 on truncation.
48A   Figure 827 on truncation, always die no. 22.

Victoria Young Head Ansell sovereign of 1859, Marsh No. 42A showing additional raised line on the lower part of the ribbon.

Victoria Young Head sovereign of 1863, Marsh No. 48A showing figure 827 on truncation.

Victoria Young Head sovereign of 1871, Marsh No. 84A.

PRICE GUIDE

Marsh No.	Date	Rarity	Type	£ NF	£ F	£ GF	£ NVF	£ VF	£ GVF	£ NEF	£ EF	£ GEF	£ UNC
84A	1871	SCARCE	YOUNG HEAD ST. GEORGE	80	85	90	95	110	140	150	175	200	300
69	1871S	COMMON	YOUNG HEAD SHIELD	70	75	80	85	95	110	135	150	225	350
110	1871S	SCARCE	YOUNG HEAD ST. GEORGE	80	85	90	95	110	150	175	225	300	400
110A	1871S	SCARCE	YOUNG HEAD ST. GEORGE	80	85	90	95	110	150	175	225	300	400
47	1872	COMMON	YOUNG HEAD SHIELD	70	75	80	85	95	110	135	150	200	250
56	1872	COMMON	YH SHIELD DIE NO.	70	75	80	85	95	110	135	150	200	250
85	1872	COMMON	YOUNG HEAD ST. GEORGE	70	75	80	85	95	105	110	130	150	200
59	1872M	RARE	YOUNG HEAD SHIELD	85	90	95	100	120	150	200	250	325	500
59A	1872/1M	RARITY 4	YOUNG HEAD SHIELD	275	350	450	600	800	1000	1500	2250	3000	3750
94	1872M	SCARCE	YOUNG HEAD ST. GEORGE	80	85	90	95	110	150	175	225	300	400
70	1872S	NORMAL	YOUNG HEAD SHIELD	75	80	85	90	120	160	200	250	325	450
111	1872S	NORMAL	YOUNG HEAD ST. GEORGE	75	80	85	90	110	130	150	200	275	350
57	1873	NORMAL	YH SHIELD DIE NO.	75	80	85	90	100	120	150	175	225	300
86	1873	SCARCE	YOUNG HEAD ST. GEORGE	80	85	90	95	110	140	150	175	200	300
95	1873M	SCARCE	YOUNG HEAD ST. GEORGE	80	85	90	95	110	150	175	225	300	400
71	1873S	SCARCE	YOUNG HEAD SHIELD	80	85	90	95	110	150	175	225	325	450
112	1873S	NORMAL	YOUNG HEAD ST. GEORGE	75	80	85	90	110	130	150	200	275	350
58	1874	RARITY 4	YH SHIELD DIE NO.	400	650	800	950	1400	1600	2000	3000	3750	4500
87	1874	RARE	YOUNG HEAD ST. GEORGE	85	90	95	100	120	140	150	175	200	275
60	1874M	NORMAL	YOUNG HEAD SHIELD	75	80	85	90	120	160	200	250	325	450
96	1874M	SCARCE	YOUNG HEAD ST. GEORGE	80	85	90	95	110	150	175	225	300	400
113	1874S	NORMAL	YOUNG HEAD ST. GEORGE	75	80	85	90	110	130	150	200	275	350
97	1875M	NORMAL	YOUNG HEAD ST. GEORGE	75	80	85	90	110	130	150	200	275	350

M84A   Large B.P. in exergue.   M110A   Large B.P. in exergue.   M59A   2 of date over 1.

Marsh No.	Date	Rarity	Type	£ NF	£ F	£ GF	£ NVF	£ VF	£ GVF	£ NEF	£ EF	£ GEF	£ UNC
72	1875S	COMMON	YOUNG HEAD SHIELD	70	75	80	85	95	110	135	150	225	350
114	1875S	NORMAL	YOUNG HEAD ST. GEORGE	75	80	85	90	110	130	150	200	275	350
88	1876	COMMON	YOUNG HEAD ST. GEORGE	70	75	80	85	95	105	110	130	150	200
98	1876M	SCARCE	YOUNG HEAD ST. GEORGE	80	85	90	95	110	150	175	225	300	400
115	1876S	SCARCE	YOUNG HEAD ST. GEORGE	80	85	90	95	140	150	175	225	300	400
99	1877M	NORMAL	YOUNG HEAD ST. GEORGE	75	80	85	90	110	130	150	200	275	350
73	1877S	NORMAL	YOUNG HEAD SHIELD	75	80	85	90	120	160	200	250	325	450
89	1878	NORMAL	YOUNG HEAD ST. GEORGE	75	80	85	90	105	120	140	155	175	225
100	1878M	COMMON	YOUNG HEAD ST. GEORGE	70	75	80	85	95	110	135	175	250	325
74	1878S	SCARCE	YOUNG HEAD SHIELD	80	85	90	95	110	150	175	225	325	450
90	1879	RARITY 4	YOUNG HEAD ST. GEORGE	110	120	130	150	175	275	475	600	950	1500
101	1879M	COMMON	YOUNG HEAD ST. GEORGE	70	75	80	85	95	110	135	175	250	325
75	1879S	NORMAL	YOUNG HEAD SHIELD	75	80	85	90	120	160	200	250	325	450
116	1879S	SCARCE	YOUNG HEAD ST. GEORGE	80	85	90	95	110	150	175	225	300	400
91	1880	COMMON	YOUNG HEAD ST. GEORGE	70	75	80	85	95	105	110	130	150	200
91A	1880/70	SCARCE	YOUNG HEAD ST. GEORGE	80	85	90	95	110	150	175	225	300	400
91B	1880/70	RARE	YOUNG HEAD ST. GEORGE	85	90	95	100	125	175	225	275	350	450
91C	1880	RARE	YOUNG HEAD ST. GEORGE	85	90	95	100	120	140	150	175	200	275
91D	1880	SCARCE	YOUNG HEAD ST. GEORGE	80	85	90	95	110	140	150	175	200	300
91E	1880	SCARCE	YOUNG HEAD ST. GEORGE	80	85	90	95	110	140	150	175	200	300
61	1880M	RARITY 2	YOUNG HEAD SHIELD	275	350	500	600	800	1250	2000	3000	3750	5000
102	1880M	NORMAL	YOUNG HEAD ST. GEORGE	75	80	85	90	110	130	150	200	275	350
76	1880S	NORMAL	YOUNG HEAD SHIELD	75	80	85	90	120	160	200	250	325	450

M91A   Second 8 of date over 7.
M91B   Second 8 of date over 7, no B.P.
M91C   No B.P. in exergue.
M91D   Large B.P. in exergue.
M91E   Small B.P. in exergue.

Left: Victoria Young Head sovereign, 1883S (Sydney), Marsh No. 120.
Right: Victoria Young Head sovereign, 1876M (Melbourne), Marsh No. 98.

Marsh No.	Date	Rarity	Type	£ NF	£ F	£ GF	£ NVF	£ VF	£ GVF	£ NEF	£ EF	£ GEF	£ UNC
117	1880S	SCARCE	YOUNG HEAD ST. GEORGE	80	85	90	95	110	150	175	225	300	400
117A	1880S	SCARCE	YOUNG HEAD ST. GEORGE	80	85	90	95	110	150	175	225	300	400
117B	1880S	SCARCE	YOUNG HEAD ST. GEORGE	80	85	90	95	110	150	175	225	300	400
62	1881M	RARE	YOUNG HEAD SHIELD	85	90	95	110	120	150	200	250	325	500
103	1881M	NORMAL	YOUNG HEAD ST. GEORGE	75	80	85	90	110	130	150	200	275	350
103A	1881M	SCARCE	YOUNG HEAD ST. GEORGE	80	85	90	95	110	150	175	225	300	400
103B	1881M	RARE	YOUNG HEAD ST. GEORGE	95	100	110	120	135	150	175	225	300	400
77	1881S	SCARCE	YOUNG HEAD SHIELD	80	85	90	95	110	150	175	225	325	450
118	1881S	SCARCE	YOUNG HEAD ST. GEORGE	80	85	90	95	110	150	175	225	300	400
118A	1881S	SCARCE	YOUNG HEAD ST. GEORGE	80	85	90	95	110	150	175	225	300	400
118B	1881S	SCARCE	YOUNG HEAD ST. GEORGE	80	85	90	95	110	150	175	225	300	400
63	1882M	SCARCE	YOUNG HEAD SHIELD	80	85	90	95	110	150	175	225	325	450
104	1882M	NORMAL	YOUNG HEAD ST. GEORGE	75	80	85	90	110	130	150	200	275	350
104A	1882M	SCARCE	YOUNG HEAD ST. GEORGE	80	85	90	95	110	150	175	225	300	400
78	1882S	NORMAL	YOUNG HEAD SHIELD	75	80	85	90	120	160	200	250	325	450
119	1882S	NORMAL	YOUNG HEAD ST. GEORGE	75	80	85	90	110	130	150	200	275	350
119A	1882S	SCARCE	YOUNG HEAD ST. GEORGE	80	85	90	95	110	150	175	225	300	400
64	1883M	RARITY 2	YOUNG HEAD SHIELD	100	125	150	175	200	250	350	500	650	900
105	1883M	NORMAL	YOUNG HEAD ST. GEORGE	75	80	85	90	110	130	150	200	275	350
79	1883S	SCARCE	YOUNG HEAD SHIELD	80	85	90	95	110	150	175	225	325	450
120	1883S	NORMAL	YOUNG HEAD ST. GEORGE	75	80	85	90	110	120	150	200	275	350
92	1884	NORMAL	YOUNG HEAD ST. GEORGE	75	80	85	90	105	120	140	155	175	225
65	1884M	NORMAL	YOUNG HEAD SHIELD	75	80	85	90	120	160	200	250	325	450

M117A	Large B.P. in exergue.	M103A	Large B.P. in exergue.
M117B	No B.P. in exergue.	M103B	No B.P. in exergue.
		M118A	Large B.P. in exergue.
		M118B	No B.P. in exergue.
		M104A	Large B.P. in exergue.
		M119A	Large B.P. in exergue.

Left: Victoria Young Head sovereign, 1871S (Sydney), Marsh No. 69.
Right: Victoria Young Head sovereign, 1884M (Melbourne), Marsh No. 65.

Marsh No.	Date	Rarity	Type	£ NF	£ F	£ GF	£ NVF	£ VF	£ GVF	£ NEF	£ EF	£ GEF	£ UNC
106	1884M	COMMON	YOUNG HEAD ST. GEORGE	70	75	80	85	95	110	135	175	250	325
80	1884S	NORMAL	YOUNG HEAD SHIELD	75	80	85	90	120	160	200	250	325	450
121	1884S	NORMAL	YOUNG HEAD ST. GEORGE	75	80	85	90	110	130	150	200	275	350
93	1885	SCARCE	YOUNG HEAD ST. GEORGE	80	85	90	95	110	140	150	175	200	300
66	1885M	NORMAL	YOUNG HEAD SHIELD	75	80	85	90	110	130	150	200	275	350
107	1885M	COMMON	YOUNG HEAD ST. GEORGE	70	75	80	85	95	110	135	175	250	325
81	1885S	SCARCE	YOUNG HEAD SHIELD	80	85	90	95	110	150	175	225	325	450
122	1885S	NORMAL	YOUNG HEAD ST. GEORGE	75	80	85	90	110	130	150	200	275	350
67	1886M	RARITY 3	YOUNG HEAD SHIELD	275	350	500	800	1250	1500	2200	3500	4500	5500
108	1886M	COMMON	YOUNG HEAD ST. GEORGE	70	75	80	85	95	110	135	175	250	325
82	1886S	SCARCE	YOUNG HEAD SHIELD	80	85	90	95	110	150	175	225	325	450
123	1886S	NORMAL	YOUNG HEAD ST. GEORGE	75	80	85	90	110	130	150	200	275	350
125	1887	NORMAL	JUBILEE HEAD	60	60	60	60	65	70	75	85	100	135
125A	1887	RARITY 2	JUBILEE HEAD	175	225	275	325	375	425	475	600	750	900
68	1887M	RARITY 3	YOUNG HEAD SHIELD	250	300	450	600	700	1000	1500	2000	2750	4000
109	1887M	COMMON	YOUNG HEAD ST. GEORGE	70	75	80	85	95	110	135	175	250	325
109A	1887M	SCARCE	YOUNG HEAD ST. GEORGE	80	85	90	95	110	150	175	225	300	400
131	1887M	SCARCE	JUBILEE HEAD	65	65	65	70	75	80	85	95	110	150
131A	1887M	SCARCE	JUBILEE HEAD	65	65	65	70	75	80	85	95	110	150
83	1887S	SCARCE	YOUNG HEAD SHIELD	80	85	90	95	110	150	175	225	325	450
124	1887S	NORMAL	YOUNG HEAD ST. GEORGE	75	80	85	90	110	130	150	200	275	350
138	1887S	SCARCE	JUBILEE HEAD	90	100	125	150	175	200	300	450	650	900
138A	1887S	SCARCE	JUBILEE HEAD	90	100	125	150	175	200	300	450	650	900

M125A   Small J.E.B. on truncation.
M109A   Large B.P. in exergue.

M131A   Small J.E.B. and with more space between.
M138A   Small J.E.B. and with more space between.

Victoria Jubilee Head sovereign, 1887M (Melbourne), Marsh No.131.

Marsh No.	Date	Rarity	Type	£ NF	£ F	£ GF	£ NVF	£ VF	£ GVF	£ NEF	£ EF	£ GEF	£ UNC
126	1888	SCARCE	JUBILEE HEAD	65	65	65	65	70	75	80	90	105	145
132	1888M	NORMAL	JUBILEE HEAD	60	60	60	60	65	70	75	85	100	135
139	1888S	NORMAL	JUBILEE HEAD	60	60	60	60	65	70	75	90	105	140
127	1889	COMMON	JUBILEE HEAD	60	60	60	60	65	70	75	80	95	130
133	1889M	NORMAL	JUBILEE HEAD	60	60	60	60	65	70	75	85	100	135
140	1889S	COMMON	JUBILEE HEAD	60	60	60	60	65	70	75	80	95	130
128	1890	COMMON	JUBILEE HEAD	60	60	60	60	65	70	75	80	95	130
134	1890M	NORMAL	JUBILEE HEAD	60	60	60	60	65	70	75	85	100	135
141	1890S	NORMAL	JUBILEE HEAD	60	60	60	60	65	70	75	85	100	135
129	1891	COMMON	JUBILEE HEAD	60	60	60	60	65	70	75	80	95	130
135	1891M	NORMAL	JUBILEE HEAD	60	60	60	60	65	70	75	85	100	135
142	1891S	NORMAL	JUBILEE HEAD	60	60	60	60	65	70	75	85	100	135
130	1892	COMMON	JUBILEE HEAD	60	60	60	60	65	70	75	80	95	130
136	1892M	NORMAL	JUBILEE HEAD	60	60	60	60	65	70	75	85	100	135
143	1892S	NORMAL	JUBILEE HEAD	60	60	60	60	65	70	75	85	100	135
145	1893	COMMON	OLD HEAD	60	60	60	60	60	60	65	75	85	100
137	1893M	SCARCE	JUBILEE HEAD	65	65	65	65	70	75	80	90	105	145
153	1893M	NORMAL	OLD HEAD	60	60	60	60	60	60	65	70	80	95
144	1893S	NORMAL	JUBILEE HEAD	60	60	60	60	65	70	75	85	100	135
162	1893S	NORMAL	OLD HEAD	60	60	60	60	60	60	65	70	80	95
146	1894	COMMON	OLD HEAD	60	60	60	60	60	60	65	70	75	90
154	1894M	COMMON	OLD HEAD	60	60	60	60	60	60	65	70	75	90
163	1894S	COMMON	OLD HEAD	60	60	60	60	60	60	65	70	75	90

Prices shown in the lower grades are subject to fluctuation in the gold price.

Victoria Old Head sovereign, 1893M (Melbourne), Marsh No.153.

Marsh No.	Date	Rarity	Type	£ NF	£ F	£ GF	£ NVF	£ VF	£ GVF	£ NEF	£ EF	£ GEF	£ UNC
147	1895	COMMON	OLD HEAD	75	75	75	75	75	75	80	100	120	150
155	1895M	COMMON	OLD HEAD	60	60	60	60	60	60	65	70	75	90
164	1895S	COMMON	OLD HEAD	60	60	60	60	60	60	65	70	75	90
148	1896	COMMON	OLD HEAD	60	60	60	60	60	60	65	70	75	90
156	1896M	COMMON	OLD HEAD	60	60	60	60	60	60	65	70	75	90
165	1896S	SCARCE	OLD HEAD	65	65	65	65	70	75	80	90	105	125
157	1897M	COMMON	OLD HEAD	60	60	60	60	60	60	65	70	75	90
166	1897S	COMMON	OLD HEAD	60	60	60	60	60	60	65	70	75	90
149	1898	COMMON	OLD HEAD	60	60	60	60	60	60	65	70	75	90
158	1898M	COMMON	OLD HEAD	60	60	60	60	60	60	65	70	75	90
167	1898S	COMMON	OLD HEAD	60	60	60	60	60	60	65	70	75	90
150	1899	COMMON	OLD HEAD	60	60	60	60	60	60	65	70	75	90
159	1899M	COMMON	OLD HEAD	60	60	60	60	60	60	65	70	75	90
171	1899P	SCARCE	OLD HEAD	65	65	65	70	75	90	125	200	300	400
168	1899S	COMMON	OLD HEAD	60	60	60	60	60	60	65	70	75	90
151	1900	COMMON	OLD HEAD	60	60	60	60	60	60	65	70	75	90
160	1900M	COMMON	OLD HEAD	60	60	60	60	60	60	65	70	75	90
172	1900P	NORMAL	OLD HEAD	60	60	60	60	60	60	65	70	90	150
169	1900S	COMMON	OLD HEAD	60	60	60	60	60	60	65	70	75	90
152	1901	NORMAL	OLD HEAD	60	60	60	60	60	60	65	70	80	95
161	1901M	COMMON	OLD HEAD	60	60	60	60	60	60	65	70	75	90
173	1901P	NORMAL	OLD HEAD	60	60	60	60	60	60	65	70	90	150
170	1901S	COMMON	OLD HEAD	60	60	60	60	60	60	65	70	75	90

Prices shown in the lower grades are subject to fluctuation in the gold price.

Left to right: Victoria Old Head sovereigns of 1898, Marsh No. 149. 1899S, Marsh No. 168. 1901P, Marsh No. 173.

Marsh No.	Date	Rarity	Type	£ NF	£ F	£ GF	£ NVF	£ VF	£ GVF	£ NEF	£ EF	£ GEF	£ UNC
174	1902	COMMON	BARE HEAD	55	55	55	55	55	55	55	55	60	75
186	1902M	COMMON	BARE HEAD	55	55	55	55	55	55	55	55	60	75
195	1902P	COMMON	BARE HEAD	55	55	55	55	55	55	55	55	60	75
204	1902S	COMMON	BARE HEAD	55	55	55	55	55	55	55	55	60	75
175	1903	COMMON	BARE HEAD	55	55	55	55	55	55	55	55	60	75
187	1903M	COMMON	BARE HEAD	55	55	55	55	55	55	55	55	60	75
196	1903P	COMMON	BARE HEAD	55	55	55	55	55	55	55	55	60	75
205	1903S	COMMON	BARE HEAD	55	55	55	55	55	55	55	55	60	75
176	1904	COMMON	BARE HEAD	55	55	55	55	55	55	55	55	60	75
188	1904M	COMMON	BARE HEAD	55	55	55	55	55	55	55	55	60	75
197	1904P	COMMON	BARE HEAD	55	55	55	55	55	55	55	55	60	75
206	1904S	COMMON	BARE HEAD	55	55	55	55	55	55	55	55	60	75
177	1905	COMMON	BARE HEAD	55	55	55	55	55	55	55	55	60	75
189	1905M	COMMON	BARE HEAD	55	55	55	55	55	55	55	55	60	75
198	1905P	COMMON	BARE HEAD	55	55	55	55	55	55	55	55	60	75
207	1905S	COMMON	BARE HEAD	55	55	55	55	55	55	55	55	60	75
178	1906	COMMON	BARE HEAD	55	55	55	55	55	55	55	55	60	75
190	1906M	COMMON	BARE HEAD	55	55	55	55	55	55	55	55	60	75
199	1906P	COMMON	BARE HEAD	55	55	55	55	55	55	55	55	60	75
208	1906S	COMMON	BARE HEAD	55	55	55	55	55	55	55	55	60	75
179	1907	COMMON	BARE HEAD	55	55	55	55	55	55	55	55	60	75
191	1907M	COMMON	BARE HEAD	55	55	55	55	55	55	55	55	60	75

Prices shown in the lower grades are subject to fluctuation in the gold price.

Edward VII sovereign of 1907, Marsh No.179.

Actual Size

Marsh No.	Date	Rarity	Type	£ NF	£ F	£ GF	£ NVF	£ VF	£ GVF	£ NEF	£ EF	£ GEF	£ UNC
200	1907P	COMMON	BARE HEAD	55	55	55	55	55	55	55	55	60	75
209	1907S	COMMON	BARE HEAD	55	55	55	55	55	55	55	55	60	75
180	1908	COMMON	BARE HEAD	55	55	55	55	55	55	55	55	60	75
183	1908C	RARITY 6	BARE HEAD							1750	2000	2500	3250
192	1908M	COMMON	BARE HEAD	55	55	55	55	55	55	55	55	60	75
201	1908P	COMMON	BARE HEAD	55	55	55	55	55	55	55	55	60	75
210	1908S	NORMAL	BARE HEAD	55	55	55	55	55	55	55	60	65	80
181	1909	COMMON	BARE HEAD	55	55	55	55	55	55	55	55	60	75
184	1909C	RARITY 2	BARE HEAD	90	95	100	110	120	130	150	175	250	350
193	1909M	COMMON	BARE HEAD	55	55	55	55	55	55	55	55	60	75
202	1909P	COMMON	BARE HEAD	55	55	55	55	55	55	55	55	60	75
211	1909S	NORMAL	BARE HEAD	55	55	55	55	55	55	55	60	65	80
182	1910	COMMON	BARE HEAD	55	55	55	55	55	55	55	55	60	75
185	1910C	RARITY 2	BARE HEAD	90	95	100	110	120	130	150	175	250	350
194	1910M	COMMON	BARE HEAD	55	55	55	55	55	55	55	55	60	75
203	1910P	COMMON	BARE HEAD	55	55	55	55	55	55	55	55	60	75
212	1910S	NORMAL	BARE HEAD	55	55	55	55	55	55	55	60	65	80

Prices shown in the lower grades are subject to fluctuation in the gold price.   M183   Satin finish proof only.

Left to right: Edward VII sovereigns, 1909C (Canada), Marsh No.184. 1907M (Melbourne), Marsh No.191.
1908P (Perth), Marsh No.201. 1909S (Sydney), Marsh No.211.

GEORGE V
1910-1936

Marsh No.	Date	Rarity	Type	£ NF	£ F	£ GF	£ NVF	£ VF	£ GVF	£ NEF	£ EF	£ GEF	£ UNC
213	1911	COMMON	LARGE HEAD	55	55	55	55	55	55	55	55	60	70
221	1911C	SCARCE	LARGE HEAD	80	80	80	85	90	95	100	120	130	150
229	1911M	COMMON	LARGE HEAD	55	55	55	55	55	55	55	55	60	70
250	1911P	COMMON	LARGE HEAD	55	55	55	55	55	55	55	55	60	70
271	1911S	COMMON	LARGE HEAD	55	55	55	55	55	55	55	55	60	70
214	1912	COMMON	LARGE HEAD	55	55	55	55	55	55	55	55	60	70
230	1912M	COMMON	LARGE HEAD	55	55	55	55	55	55	55	55	60	70
251	1912P	COMMON	LARGE HEAD	55	55	55	55	55	55	55	55	60	70
272	1912S	COMMON	LARGE HEAD	55	55	55	55	55	55	55	55	60	70
215	1913	COMMON	LARGE HEAD	55	55	55	55	55	55	55	55	60	70
222	1913C	RARITY 4	LARGE HEAD	100	125	150	200	300	375	450	600	800	1200
231	1913M	COMMON	LARGE HEAD	55	55	55	55	55	55	55	55	60	70
252	1913P	COMMON	LARGE HEAD	55	55	55	55	55	55	55	55	60	70
273	1913S	COMMON	LARGE HEAD	55	55	55	55	55	55	55	55	60	70
216	1914	COMMON	LARGE HEAD	55	55	55	55	55	55	55	55	60	70
223	1914C	RARITY 3	LARGE HEAD	90	115	135	150	200	250	300	375	500	600
232	1914M	COMMON	LARGE HEAD	55	55	55	55	55	55	55	55	60	70
253	1914P	COMMON	LARGE HEAD	55	55	55	55	55	55	55	55	60	70
274	1914S	COMMON	LARGE HEAD	55	55	55	55	55	55	55	55	60	70
217	1915	COMMON	LARGE HEAD	55	55	55	55	55	55	55	55	60	70
233	1915M	NORMAL	LARGE HEAD	55	55	55	55	55	55	55	55	65	75
254	1915P	COMMON	LARGE HEAD	55	55	55	55	55	55	55	55	60	70

Prices shown in the lower grades are subject to fluctuation in the gold price.

George V sovereign of 1911, Marsh No.213.   *Actual Size*

Marsh No.	Date	Rarity	Type	£ NF	£ F	£ GF	£ NVF	£ VF	£ GVF	£ NEF	£ EF	£ GEF	£ UNC
275	1915S	SCARCE	LARGE HEAD	55	55	55	55	55	55	55	60	70	80
218	1916	RARE	LARGE HEAD	60	60	60	60	60	60	65	70	80	90
224	1916C	RARITY 5	LARGE HEAD	1000	1500	2000	3000	4200	5000	7500	9000	12000	15000
234	1916M	NORMAL	LARGE HEAD	55	55	55	55	55	55	55	55	65	75
255	1916P	SCARCE	LARGE HEAD	55	55	55	55	55	55	55	60	70	80
276	1916S	NORMAL	LARGE HEAD	55	55	55	55	55	55	55	55	65	75
219	1917	RARITY 5	LARGE HEAD	750	900	1100	1500	1800	2250	3000	3750	5000	6500
225	1917C	RARE	LARGE HEAD	90	95	100	110	120	130	140	150	160	175
235	1917M	SCARCE	LARGE HEAD	55	55	55	55	55	55	55	60	70	80
256	1917P	SCARCE	LARGE HEAD	55	55	55	55	55	55	55	60	70	80
277	1917S	COMMON	LARGE HEAD	55	55	55	55	55	55	55	55	60	70
226	1918C	SCARCE	LARGE HEAD	85	90	95	100	110	120	130	140	150	175
228	1918I	NORMAL	LARGE HEAD	60	60	60	60	60	60	65	70	80	90
236	1918M	COMMON	LARGE HEAD	55	55	55	55	55	55	55	55	60	70
257	1918P	COMMON	LARGE HEAD	55	55	55	55	55	55	55	55	60	70
278	1918S	COMMON	LARGE HEAD	55	55	55	55	55	55	55	55	60	70
227	1919C	SCARCE	LARGE HEAD	85	90	95	100	110	120	130	140	150	175
237	1919M	SCARCE	LARGE HEAD	60	60	60	60	60	60	65	70	80	90
258	1919P	COMMON	LARGE HEAD	55	55	55	55	55	55	55	55	60	70
279	1919S	NORMAL	LARGE HEAD	55	55	55	55	55	55	55	55	65	75
238	1920M	RARITY 2	LARGE HEAD	400	500	600	750	900	1100	1500	2000	3000	4000
259	1920P	COMMON	LARGE HEAD	55	55	55	55	55	55	55	55	60	70

Prices shown in the lower grades are subject to fluctuation in the gold price.

George V sovereigns, 1913C (Canada), Marsh No.222. 1918I (India), Marsh No.228.

Marsh No.	Date	Rarity	Type	£ NF	£ F	£ GF	£ NVF	£ VF	£ GVF	£ NEF	£ EF	£ GEF	£ UNC
280	1920S	RARITY 3	LARGE HEAD										
239	1921M	RARITY 3	LARGE HEAD	700	900	1100	1500	2000	2750	3500	4500	6000	7500
260	1921P	COMMON	LARGE HEAD	55	55	55	55	55	55	55	55	60	70
281	1921S	RARITY 3	LARGE HEAD	300	400	500	600	750	900	1100	1600	2250	3250
240	1922M	RARITY 2	LARGE HEAD	600	750	900	1100	1500	2000	2500	4000	6000	7500
261	1922P	COMMON	LARGE HEAD	55	55	55	55	55	55	55	55	60	70
282	1922S	RARITY 3	LARGE HEAD	1000	1500	2000	3000	4000	6000	9500	12000	15000	200000
241	1923M	RARE	LARGE HEAD	55	55	55	65	75	85	90	95	100	125
262	1923P	COMMON	LARGE HEAD	55	55	55	55	55	55	55	55	60	70
287	1923SA	RARITY 6	LARGE HEAD	175	225	300	400	500	650	900	1200	1750	2500
283	1923S	RARITY 4	LARGE HEAD	600	750	1000	1500	2200	3000	3750	5000	6500	9000
242	1924M	RARE	LARGE HEAD	55	55	55	65	75	85	90	95	100	125
263	1924P	NORMAL	LARGE HEAD	65	70	75	80	90	100	125	150	200	300
288	1924SA	RARITY 5	LARGE HEAD	450	550	700	900	1100	1350	1800	2250	3000	3500
284	1924S	RARITY 3	LARGE HEAD	300	350	400	500	600	750	900	1100	1500	2000
220	1925	COMMON	LARGE HEAD	55	55	55	55	55	55	55	55	60	70
243	1925M	COMMON	LARGE HEAD	55	55	55	55	55	55	55	55	60	70
264	1925P	SCARCE	LARGE HEAD	65	70	75	80	90	100	125	175	250	375
285	1925S	SCARCE	LARGE HEAD	55	55	55	55	55	55	55	60	70	80
289	1925SA	COMMON	LARGE HEAD	55	55	55	55	55	55	55	55	60	70

Prices shown in the lower grades are subject to fluctuation in the gold price.

M280   A good EF specimen sold
at auction in March 1992 for £104,000 plus buyer's premium.

Left to right: George V sovereigns, 1918M (Melbourne),
Marsh No.236. 1918P (Perth), Marsh No.257. 1925SA (South Africa), Marsh No.289.

Marsh No.	Date	Rarity	Type	£ NF	£ F	£ GF	£ NVF	£ VF	£ GVF	£ NEF	£ EF	£ GEF	£ UNC
244	1926M	RARE	LARGE HEAD	55	55	55	65	75	85	90	95	100	125
265	1926P	RARE	LARGE HEAD	90	100	150	200	300	400	500	650	900	1200
290	1926SA	COMMON	LARGE HEAD	55	55	55	55	55	55	55	55	60	70
286	1926S	RARITY 4	LARGE HEAD	1500	2000	2500	3500	4500	6500	10000	12500	16000	22000
266	1927P	SCARCE	LARGE HEAD	65	70	75	80	90	100	125	175	250	350
291	1927SA	COMMON	LARGE HEAD	55	55	55	55	55	55	55	55	60	70
246	1928M	RARITY 2	LARGE HEAD	400	500	600	750	900	1100	1500	1750	2250	3000
267	1928P	SCARCE	LARGE HEAD	65	65	70	75	80	90	100	150	175	250
292	1928SA	COMMON	LARGE HEAD	55	55	55	55	55	55	55	55	60	70
247	1929M	RARITY 3	SMALL HEAD	400	500	600	750	900	1100	1500	1750	2250	3000
268	1929P	SCARCE	SMALL HEAD	55	55	55	55	55	55	55	60	70	80
293	1929SA	COMMON	SMALL HEAD	55	55	55	55	55	55	55	55	60	70
248	1930M	RARE	SMALL HEAD	80	80	80	80	90	100	125	175	250	350
269	1930P	RARE	SMALL HEAD	55	55	55	65	75	85	90	95	100	125
294	1930SA	COMMON	SMALL HEAD	55	55	55	55	55	55	55	55	60	70
249	1931M	RARITY 2	SMALL HEAD	100	110	120	130	150	175	200	300	400	600
270	1931P	SCARCE	SMALL HEAD	55	55	55	55	55	55	55	60	70	80
295	1931SA	COMMON	SMALL HEAD	55	55	55	55	55	55	55	60	65	75
296	1932SA	NORMAL	SMALL HEAD	55	55	55	55	55	55	75	95	100	115

Prices shown in the lower grades are subject to fluctuation in the gold price.

George V sovereign, 1930P (Perth), Marsh No.269.

74

ELIZABETH II
1952-

PRICE GUIDE

Marsh No.	Date	Rarity	Type	£ NF	£ F	£ GF	£ NVF	£ VF	£ GVF	£ NEF	£ EF	£ GEF	£ UNC	Proof
297	1957	NORMAL	SECOND ISSUE								80	85	75	
298	1958	COMMON	SECOND ISSUE								55	55	85	
299	1959	NORMAL	SECOND ISSUE								55	55	70	
300	1962	COMMON	SECOND ISSUE								55	55	70	
301	1963	COMMON	SECOND ISSUE								55	55	70	
302	1964	COMMON	SECOND ISSUE								55	55	70	
303	1965	COMMON	SECOND ISSUE								55	55	70	
304	1966	COMMON	SECOND ISSUE								55	55	70	
305	1967	COMMON	SECOND ISSUE								55	55	70	
306	1968	COMMON	SECOND ISSUE								55	55	70	
307	1974	COMMON	THIRD ISSUE								55	55	65	
308	1976	COMMON	THIRD ISSUE								55	55	65	
309	1978	COMMON	THIRD ISSUE								55	55	65	
310	1979	COMMON	THIRD ISSUE								55	55	65	85
311	1980	COMMON	THIRD ISSUE								55	55	65	85
312	1981	COMMON	THIRD ISSUE								55	55	65	85
313	1982	COMMON	THIRD ISSUE								55	55	65	85
	1983		THIRD ISSUE											120
	1984		THIRD ISSUE											125
	1985		FOURTH ISSUE											135
	1986		FOURTH ISSUE											135
	1987		FOURTH ISSUE											135

Prices shown in the lower grades are subject to fluctuation in the gold price.   M298   Coarser graining on edge.

Elizabeth II sovereign of 1962, Marsh No.300.

Marsh No.	Date	Rarity	Type	£ NF	£ F	£ GF	£ NVF	£ VF	£ GVF	£ NEF	£ EF	£ GEF	£ UNC	Proof
	1988		FOURTH ISSUE											135
	1989		FOURTH ISSUE											135
	1990		FOURTH ISSUE											150
	1991		FOURTH ISSUE											150
	1992		FOURTH ISSUE											150
	1993		FOURTH ISSUE											150
	1994		FOURTH ISSUE											150
	1995		FOURTH ISSUE											150
	1996		FOURTH ISSUE											150
	1997		FOURTH ISSUE											150
	1998		FIFTH ISSUE											150
	1999		FIFTH ISSUE											150
	2000		FIFTH ISSUE										70	150

Elizabeth II sovereigns of 1974, Marsh No.307. 1989 and 2000.

Further reading and information

The Gold Sovereign,

by Michael Marsh, Cambridge, Second Edition 1999.
The best and easiest-to follow guide to the sovereign. The book has a number of enlarged photographs,
and the date listing is clear and precise.

Royal Sovereign, 1489-1989,

Graham P. Dyer (editor), London, 1989.
This book was published by the Royal Mint to celebrate the 500th anniversary of the introduction of the sovereign into
the British coinage, and is a series of five excellent essays, with splendid illustrations throughout.

The History of the Gold Sovereign,

by Sir Geoffrey Duveen and H. G. Stride, London, 1962.
Duveen, well known for his fine art dealing, was also a collector of coins, whilst Stride,
Deputy Master of the Royal Mint, was his mentor.

A New History of the Royal Mint,

Christopher E. Challis (editor), London 1992.
A major work with contributions from a number of respected numismatists, and many illustrations and tables.

The Mint: A History of the London Mint from AD 287 to 1948,

by Sir John Craig, Cambridge, 1953.

Sovereigns of the British Empire,

by J. J. Cullimore Allen, London, 1965.

Other more general guides to British Coins are published, some annually, others less frequently.

Standard Catalogue of British Coins – Coins of England and the United Kingdom,

Spink Publications, London, 2001.

Coincraft's Standard Catalogue of English and UK Coins, 1066 to Date,

by Richard Lobel, Mark Davidson, Allan Hailstone and Eleni Calligas, Coincraft, London, 2000.

Gold Sovereign
Second Edition 1999
Michael A Marsh

Michael A. Marsh has been a keen student of modern British gold for more than 40 years, and for much of this time he has settled on the study of the gold sovereign, which must surely be the world's most famous gold coin.

Michael is now firmly recognised world-wide as an authority on the sovereign. Since 1980 he has written and published five books, all of which are closely associated with his chosen study. The first of these was the first edition of *The Gold Sovereign* released in 1980. In 1982 *The Gold Half Sovereign* appeared and this was the first time that a whole book had been devoted entirely to this coin. Later that year the author produced a beautiful handbound updated Special Edition of his first two books.

In 1996 came the piece de resistance for all interested in our modern gold coinage when Michael published *Benedetto Pistrucci Principal Engraver and Chief Medallist of the Royal Mint 1783-1855*. This is a comprehensive history of a truly great engraver and of course the book reveals how Pistrucci designed and engraved the first of our modern gold sovereigns in 1817. This coin with its magnificent reverse of St. George slaying the Dragon has gone on and on through time and St. George is still proudly featured on our current sovereign. Finally in August of last year Michael has designed and written book number five, and it is a fully updated second edition of *The Gold Sovereign*. The text of well over 30,000 words is rich in historical content and begins at the reign of Henry VII in 1489, and goes on to reveal many important changes introduced and effected by The Royal Mint and its engravers

over a long period of time. Every known sovereign is listed, including all three exciting new sovereigns of our present Queen Elizabeth II. All have been carefully introduced into the new book simply by using the letters A, B, C and D in appropriate places, thus enabling Michael to retain the same numbering, date, variety, mintage and rarity layout he had introduced and established in the 1980 first edition. There are 59 superb plates of which 20 are in full colour and most of the rare sovereigns within the series are featured. Amongst those included is the Type 1A sovereign overdate 1843/2 M.A.M.26B, and this was the first overdate to be established within the sovereign series from the London Mint. After many years of searching Michael finally found the elusive overdate in 1981, and he duly published it and it was recorded in the Royal Mint records. However, to assist in the identification of this exciting new discovery he found it necessary to use for the first time in the numismatic field the electronic scanning microscope. This wonderful piece of modern technology proved beyond doubt that at last it was possible to record an overdate within the sovereign series. The pictures taken by its camera produced clear evidence of this, as I am sure you will enjoy when you study them within the plates of *The Gold Sovereign*. This superb casebound second edition is a must for all collectors, and is certainly for those who enjoy the sheer beauty and fascination of the gold sovereign. If you would like to add this important new second edition of *The Gold Sovereign* to your library; long since recognised as the standard work, then you will note the full details of the book are shown below together with all other Michael Marsh Publications that are currently available.

M A MARSH (Publications)
25A St. Neots Road, Hardwick, Cambridgeshire CB3 7QH

THE GOLD SOVEREIGN 2ND Edition
£15 + p&p £2.50. Airmail: Europe £3.50, USA £5.75, rest of world £7.85

THE GOLD SOVEREIGN (Special Ed.)
£30 + p&p £2.75. Airmail: Europe £3.75, USA £5.75, rest of world £7.75

THE BENEDETTO PISTRUCCI HISTORY 1783-1855
£9.85 + p&p £1.75. Airmail: Europe £2.50, USA £4.00, rest of world £5.50

THE BENEDETTO PISTRUCCI HISTORY (Special Ed.)
£22.50 + p&p £2.75. Airmail: Europe £3.25, USA £5.50, rest of world £7.50

THE GOLD HALF SOVEREIGN
£7.50 + p&p £1.50. Airmail: Europe £2.25, rest of world £4.25

Brian Reeds (Coins)

Specialising in English hammered, milled gold, silver and copper coins.

The Perfect gift

The sovereign is one of the world's best-known gold coins. In its modern form it was first struck in 1817 during the reign of George III. The reverse depicts the classical portrayal by Benedetto Pistrucci of St. George on horseback slaying the Dragon. The first part of Queen Victoria where the reverse was an armorial design, which gave rise to the name "Shield Back", a name which continues to be used today. The sovereign is struck in 22 carat gold; it has a diameter of 22 millimetres and a weight of 7.9881 grams. It was to be the coin that would set the standard for world trade for a century, only giving way to paper money at the end of the Great War, and finally becoming a part of our numismatic heritage when the country came off the gold standard in the 1930s.

With world-wide interest in historic gold sovereigns, these original pieces of British history will make a perfect gift for Christmas or special occasions such as a christening or birthday. If you are looking for a particular date, for whatever celebration, please contact me at the Freepost address.

S & B's Coin & Medal Bulletin

Bi-monthly issue contains articles, news and views of interest to collectors, together with a listing of selected medals, tokens, English hammered and milled coins from our stock. Many of the coins listed are also illustrated.

Review a copy of our S & B bulletin prior to subscribing; contact us for a complimentary copy.

Annual subscription rates 6 issues, including postage
UK: 2ND Class Mail £6.00
EUROPE: 1ST Class Mail £8.00
WORLD: Air Mail £10.00 or US$18

Brian Reeds (Coins)
Freepost, SCE201, Great Missenden, Bucks, HP16 0BR
Phone: 01494 891040
Fax: 01494 890940
Mobile: 07973 227498
E-mail: brian@sovereigns4u.co.uk

Daniel Fearon

Dealer and Auction Consultant, specialising in coins, medals and medallions.

Offering professional and independent advice, Daniel Fearon, formerly head of the Coin and Medal Department at Bonhams, will provide valuations on coins, medals or medallions for sale, auction, appraisal or insurance purposes.

He also offers a specialist cataloguing service and will act as a confidential bidding agent at auctions, whether in the saleroom or on the internet.

Daniel Fearon
9, Coombe House Chase
New Malden
Surrey
KT3 4SL

Phone: 020 8942 5747
E-mail: info@danielfearon.com

ROYAL MINT

The gold sovereign is arguably the most prestigious coin produced by the Royal Mint.
First struck more than five hundred years ago during the reign of Henry VII when the Mint
occupied premises within the Tower of London, it was, from the start, a coin of beauty
and distinction. But as the pages of this book have shown, it enjoyed its heyday in
the reign of Queen Victoria, when it was truly the chief coin of the world. Its existence was
subsequently threatened by world war but such has been its enduring appeal that it
continues to be struck today – to the delight of coin collectors, to
whom, indeed, it seems the symbol of Britain herself.

Each year, therefore, the Royal Mint produces sovereigns for collectors,
sovereigns whose weight and composition have been unchanged since 1817 and whose reverse
is still graced by Pistrucci's classically beautiful design of St George and the Dragon.

Royal Mint

Llantrisant, Pontyclun, CF72 8YT
www.royalmint.com